Help with homework

Maths

essentials

HI, MY NAME IS KITCAT...

... AND I'M DIG.

WE ARE HERE TO HELP YOU THROUGH THESE EXERCISES. START AT THE BEGINNING OF THE BOOK AND DON'T DO TOO MUCH IN ONE GO.

IT WON'T BE EASY ALL OF THE TIME – SOME PAGES CAN BE TRICKY, BUT WE'VE GIVEN YOU THE ANSWERS AT THE END OF THIS SECTION, JUST IN CASE YOU GET REALLY STUCK. NO PEEPING THOUGH! YOU WILL FIND LOTS OF PAGES FOR YOUR WORKINGS OUT AFTER THE ANSWER PAGES... GOOD LUCK!

Written by Nina Filipek
Designed and illustrated by Dan Green
Cover design by Dan Green

www.autumnchildrensbooks.co.uk

number values

Write these numbers in words.

For example:
321,857 = three hundred and twenty-one thousand, eight hundred and fifty-seven

a. 53 _____

b. 653 _____

c. 1653 _____

d. 21,653 _____

e. 721,653 _____

Write these numbers in numerals.

a. Two thousand, three hundred and four _____

b. Nine thousand, one hundred and eighty _____

c. Eleven thousand, three hundred and seventy-six _____

d. Fifty thousand, six hundred and four _____

e. Two hundred and one thousand, eight hundred and ninety _____

Order these numbers from the smallest to the biggest.

a. 7436, 5345, 4201, 6032 _____

b. 5642, 5386, 5740, 5900 _____

c. 6945, 6201, 6001, 6389 _____

get it?

To order the digits, start from the left each time.

When you order decimal numbers, it can help if you line them up underneath each other.

For example:

0.60
0.06

0.60 is bigger than 0.06

get it?

0.06 is "nought point nought six".

0.60 is "nought point six nought".

Order these decimals from the smallest to the biggest.

a. 0.01, 0.90, 0.59, 0.73 _____

b. 0.10, 0.05, 0.21, 0.09 _____

Complete this number line with negative numbers.

-10   -8 -7   -5 -4   -1 0 1 2 3 4 5 6 7 8 9 10

Order these numbers as they would appear on the number line.

a. 9, 10, -1, -7, -3, -10 _____

b. 7, -7, 4, -2, -1, 9 _____

c. 5, 0, -1, 1, -8, -4 _____

addition and subtraction

Add the units first, then add the tens, then the hundreds and finally the thousands.

Remember to carry digits over to the correct columns.

For example:

Th	H	T	U
	1	4	5	5
+		2	3	5
1	6	9	0
			1

5 + 5 = 10 so carry the ten into the tens column.

Add these numbers.

a

	H	T	U
	5	7	3
+	3	3	5

b

	H	T	U
	6	7	5
+	2	1	5

c

	Th	H	T	U
	1	2	4	3
+	1	8	0	7

d

	Th	H	T	U
	2	4	7	2
+	1	1	5	5

e

	Th	H	T	U
	6	0	3	4
+	1	2	6	5

f

	Th	H	T	U
	5	1	4	2
+	1	3	6	8

Subtract the units first, then subtract the tens, hundreds and finally the thousands.

If you don't have enough units, exchange (or borrow) a ten for 10 units. If you don't have enough tens, exchange a hundred for 10 tens. If you don't have enough hundreds, exchange a thousand for 10 hundreds.

For example:

	Th	H	T	U
	$\overset{0}{\cancel{1}}$	$\overset{15}{\cancel{6}}$	$\overset{12}{\cancel{3}}$	$\overset{1}{2}$
−		7	4	5
		8	8	7

Subtract these numbers.

a

```
    H  T  U
    6  4  3
 -  3  5  4
_____

_____
```

b

```
    H  T  U
    6  7  2
 -  2  2  4
_____

_____
```

c

```
 Th H  T  U
  1  2  9  0
 -     7  2  7
_____

_____
```

d

```
 Th H  T  U
  2  2  8  9
 -  1  1  9  5
_____

_____
```

e

```
 Th H  T  U
  3  7  7  7
 -  1  2  7  5
_____

_____
```

f

```
 Th H  T  U
  4  0  2  4
 -  1  1  9  5
_____

_____
```

get it?

Start from the right each time. You can exchange or borrow from the columns to the left.

1 ten = 10 units

1 hundred = 10 tens

1 thousand = 10 hundreds

shapes

Learn the names of these 2-dimensional (2-D) shapes.

Can you draw lines of symmetry on each shape?

Parallelogram – opposite sides are equal and parallel

Trapezium – 2 sides are parallel

Square – 4 sides are equal, and 4 right angles

Rectangle – opposite sides are equal, 4 right angles

Regular pentagon – 5 equal sides, 5 equal angles

Regular hexagon – 6 equal sides, 6 equal angles

Rhombus – 4 equal sides, opposite sides are parallel

Kite – adjacent sides are equal, no sides are parallel

Answer: True (T) or False (F) below.

1. A square has 4 equal sides and 4 equal angles. ☐

2. A rectangle has equal opposite sides. ☐

3. A square is a quadrilateral. ☐

4. A trapezium has 1 line of symmetry. ☐

5. A rectangle has 4 lines of symmetry. ☐

A QUADRILATERAL IS A SHAPE THAT HAS FOUR SIDES.

Learn the names of these 3-dimensional (3-D) shapes.

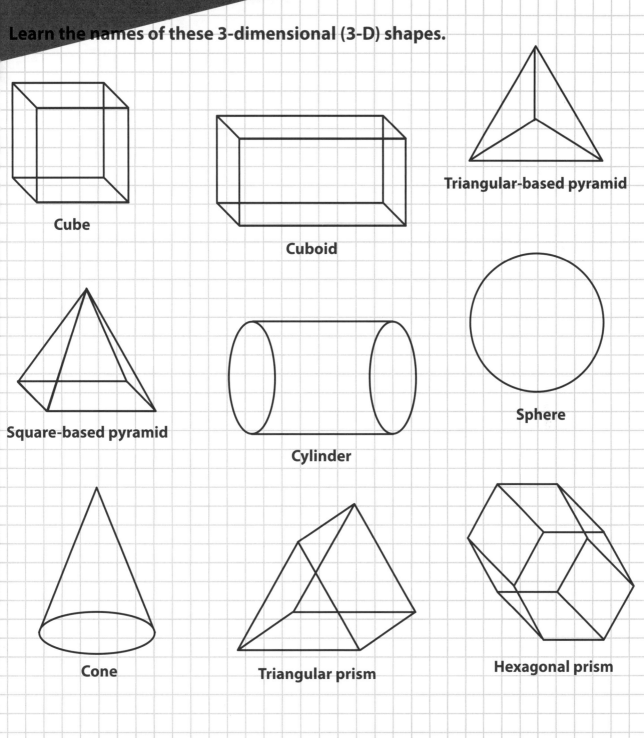

Cube

Cuboid

Triangular-based pyramid

Square-based pyramid

Cylinder

Sphere

Cone

Triangular prism

Hexagonal prism

Complete the table below:

Shape	Number of faces	Number of edges	Number of corners (vertices)
Cube			
Square-based pyramid			
Triangular prism			
Cylinder			

multiples and factors

A **multiple** is the number you get when you multiply one number with another number, for example the multiples of 5 are 5, 10, 15, 20, 25, etc.

Count in 3s:

3 — 6 — ◯ — 12 — ◯ — ◯ — 21 — ◯ — 27 — ◯

Count in 4s:

◯ — 8 — ◯ — ◯ — 20 — 24 — ◯ — 32 — ◯ — 40

Count in 6s:

6 — 12 — ◯ — 24 — ◯ — 36 — ◯ — 48 — ◯ — 60

Count in 8s:

8 — 16 — ◯ — ◯ — 40 — 48 — ◯ — ◯ — 72 — 80

Circle the numbers that are multiples of 3. Which two numbers are also multiples of 6?

32   36   40   9   30   27   21

Circle the numbers that are multiples of 4. Which three numbers are also multiples of 8?

24   40   80   28   46   15   36

8

A **factor** is a number that will divide evenly (without a remainder) into another number, for example 3 is a factor of 6, 9 and 12, etc.

Find all the factors of 36:

1 x 36

2 x 18

3 x ___

4 x ___

6 x ___

Find all the factors of 24:

1 x 24

2 x ___

3 x ___

4 x ___

A **prime number** is only divisible by 1 and itself, eg 3 is a prime number.

Which of these are prime numbers? Circle them.

| 11 | 15 | 5 | 13 | 7 | 10 | 9 | 12 |

Work out what the missing numbers are.

For example:

6

3   2

49

7   ○

28

4   ○

30

15   ○

35

5   ○

15

4

12

9

3

get it?

even x even = even

odd x odd = odd

odd x even = even

16

7

division and multiplication

Complete the multiplication grid.

The first answer is done to get you started.

X	7	5	6	2
3	21			
6				
8				
4				

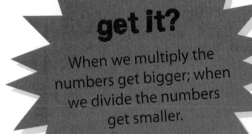

get it?

When we multiply the numbers get bigger; when we divide the numbers get smaller.

Multiplication and division are **opposites**.

For example:
8 x 5 = 40, so 40 ÷ 8 = 5 and 40 ÷ 5 = 8

Write two divisions to match each multiplication.

5 x 6 = 30

30 ÷ 6 = 5

30 ÷ ___ = ___

5 x 11 = 55

55 ÷ ___ = ___

55 ÷ ___ = ___

7 x 4 = 28

28 ÷ ___ = ___

28 ÷ ___ = ___

8 x 6 = 48

48 ÷ ___ = ___

48 ÷ ___ = ___

Division is like **repeated subtraction**.

For example:
55 ÷ 11 = 5 is the same as: 55 − 11 − 11 − 11 − 11 − 11

Work out these divisions.

30 ÷ 5 = ___

30 −

70 ÷ 10 = ___

70 −

56 ÷ 7 = ___

56 −

You can work out divisions using repeated subtraction on a number line.

For example:

12 ÷ 3 = __4__

12 11 10 9 8 7 6 5 4 3 2 1 0

Try it for yourself.

15 ÷ 3 = ___

15 14 13 12 11 10 9 8 7 6 5 4 3 2 1 0

20 ÷ 5 = ___

20 19 18 17 16 15 14 13 12 11 10 9 8 7 6 5 4 3 2 1 0

perimeter and area

The **perimeter** is the distance around the edges of a shape.

Find the perimeter of these shapes.

a Perimeter = _____ cm

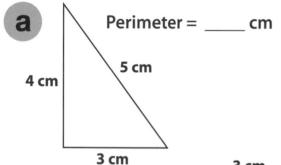
4 cm
5 cm
3 cm

b

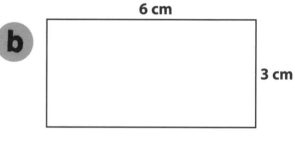
6 cm
3 cm

Perimeter = _____ cm

c Perimeter = _____ cm

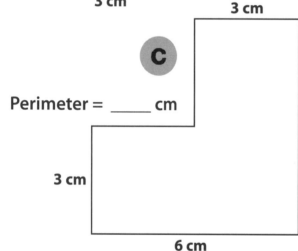
3 cm
3 cm
6 cm

d

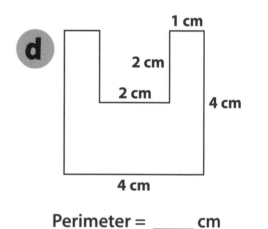
1 cm
2 cm
2 cm
4 cm
4 cm

Perimeter = _____ cm

Measure these shapes and find the perimeter.

a

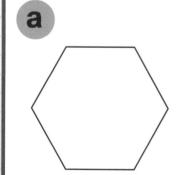

Perimeter = _____ cm

b

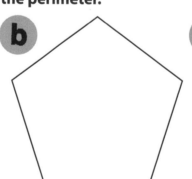

Perimeter = _____ cm

c

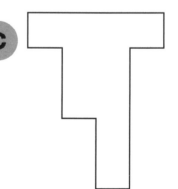

Perimeter = _____ cm

The **area** is the measurement of the space inside the shape.
To find the area of a shape you multiply the length by the width.

For example:
This rectangle has an area of 8 cm².

4 cm

2 cm

get it?

Area = length x width

So, 4 x 2 = 8 cm².

Find the area of these shapes.

You might have to divide complex shapes into rectangles to work out the area.

a

5 cm

15 cm

b

20 cm

8 cm

c

5 cm

10 cm

5 cm

d

8 cm

8 cm

4 cm

4 cm

2 cm

QUESTION:
HOW DO YOU FIND THE
AREA OF THIS TRIANGLE?

2 cm

3 cm

ANSWER:
FIND THE AREA OF
THE RECTANGLE
AND THEN HALVE
YOUR ANSWER.
EASY!

fractions and percentages

$\frac{1}{4}$ means 1 part out of 4 equal parts.

$\frac{3}{4}$ means 3 parts out of 4 equal parts.

What fraction of these shapes is shaded?

b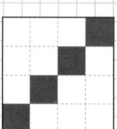

c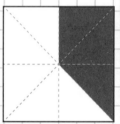

You can **simplify** fractions if you can divide the top number and the bottom number by the same factor.

For example:

$\frac{2}{6} = \frac{1}{3}$

Divide the numerator $\quad 2 \div 2 = 1$

Divide the denominator $\quad 6 \div 2 = 3$

THE TOP NUMBER IS CALLED THE *NUMERATOR*. THE BOTTOM NUMBER IS CALLED THE *DENOMINATOR*.

Simplify these fractions:

a. $\frac{4}{10} = $— **b.** $\frac{3}{6} = $— **c.** $\frac{8}{16} = $— **d.** $\frac{4}{16} = $—

e. $\frac{5}{10} = $— **f.** $\frac{2}{10} = $— **g.** $\frac{3}{12} = $— **h.** $\frac{4}{12} = $—

get it?

$\frac{6}{6}$ is one whole. $\frac{10}{10}$ is one whole. $\frac{12}{12}$ is one whole.

A **percentage** is a part of a hundred.

Learn these fraction and percentage equivalents.

10% or $\frac{1}{10}$									
20% or $\frac{1}{5}$									
25% or $\frac{1}{4}$									
50% or $\frac{1}{2}$									
100% or 1 whole									

Work out the answers.

get it?

1% is 1/100

10% is 10/100

20% is 20/100

a. $\frac{1}{2}$ of 50 = ____

b. 50% of 30 = ____

c. $\frac{1}{4}$ of 4 = ____

d. 25% of 8 = ____

e. $\frac{1}{5}$ of £2.50 = ____p

f. 20% of £5 = £____

g. $\frac{2}{5}$ of 25p = ____p

h. 40% of 30p = ____p

i. 10% of £4 = ____p

j. $\frac{1}{10}$ of £8 = ____p

15

fractions

Colour $\frac{1}{4}$ of this circle red.

Colour $\frac{1}{2}$ of this circle blue.

What is the total fraction coloured?

Which is bigger?

A slice that is $\frac{2}{3}$ or $\frac{3}{4}$ of this pizza?

Colour the pizza to work it out.

Which is bigger?

a. $\frac{5}{8}$ or $\frac{1}{4}$? _____

b. $\frac{3}{8}$ or $\frac{3}{4}$? _____

c. $\frac{4}{12}$ or $\frac{4}{6}$? _____

d. $\frac{5}{12}$ or $\frac{2}{3}$? _____

e. $\frac{4}{6}$ or $\frac{1}{3}$? _____

get it?

A **fraction** is an equal part of a whole.

Write these fractions in the correct place on the number line below.

get it?
$\frac{5}{10}$ and $\frac{1}{2}$ are **equivalent** fractions!

0 |——|——|——|——|——|——|——|——|——|——| 1

$\frac{1}{2}$ $\frac{1}{5}$ $\frac{10}{10}$ $\frac{1}{10}$ $\frac{7}{10}$ $\frac{2}{5}$ $\frac{3}{10}$ $\frac{4}{5}$ $\frac{5}{10}$

Which two fractions have the same value?

Join the equivalent fractions with a line.

$\frac{2}{3}$ $\frac{2}{4}$ $\frac{3}{12}$ $\frac{3}{9}$

$\frac{4}{6}$ $\frac{1}{4}$ $\frac{1}{3}$ $\frac{1}{2}$

Order these fractions from the smallest to the biggest.

$\frac{1}{2}$ $\frac{1}{4}$ $\frac{3}{4}$ $\frac{4}{10}$

WHAT DID ONE FRACTION SAY TO THE OTHER FRACTION? "YOU DON'T KNOW THE HALF OF IT!"

( ) — ( ) — ( ) — ( )

smallest
fraction

biggest
fraction

17

angles and triangles

An **angle** is a rotation around a point.
We can measure an angle using a protractor.

There are four types of angles.

Right angle:
a quarter turn (90°)

Acute angle:
less than a quarter turn
(less than 90°)

Reflex: more than half
a turn (more than 180°
but less than 360°)

Obtuse: between a
quarter and a half turn
(more than 90° but less
than 180°)

* A complete rotation around a point is 360°.

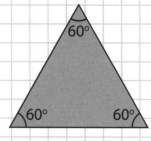

Isosceles: 2 equal sides
and 2 equal angles

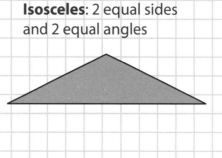

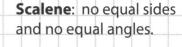

Equilateral: 3 equal sides
and 3 equal angles

Scalene: no equal sides
and no equal angles.

Right-angled:
one right-angle

get it?

If you are given two angles, say 70° and 80°, you add these together and subtract them from 180 to find the missing angle.
180-150 = 30°.

If you add up the angles in a triangle you always get 180°.

Work out the missing angles in these triangles.

a. 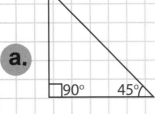 _____

b. 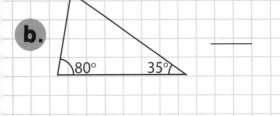 _____

c. _____

d. 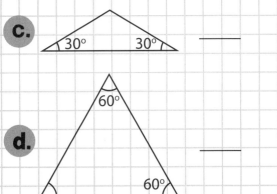 _____

Label these angles: acute, right-angle, obtuse or reflex.

a.  _____

b. _____

c. _____

d. _____

Find the angles.

a. 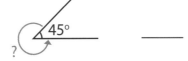 45° _____

b.  180° _____

c. 90° _____

d. 270° _____

coordinates

Coordinates are the numbers we use to mark a point on a graph or map.

When reading coordinates, remember to *'go along the corridor and up (or down) the stairs'*.

Plot these positions on the graph.

a. (-2, 2) **b.** (-4, 4) **c.** (2, 2) **d.** (4, 4)

e. (-2, -2) **f.** (-4, -4) **g.** (2, -2) **h.** (4, -4)

get it?

Another way to remember how to read coordinates: x comes before y in the alphabet, so read the x axis first then the y axis.

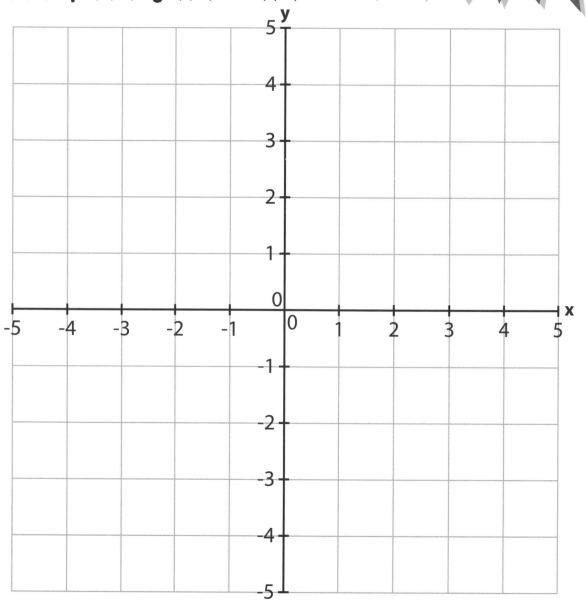

Write the coordinates of the buried bone: (_____ , _____)

Draw another bone on the map and write its coordinates here: (_____ , _____)

Plot these coordinates to find a hidden shape.

(-4, -4) (-4, 2) (-2, 4) (-2, -2)

NOW WHERE
DID I PUT
THAT BONE?

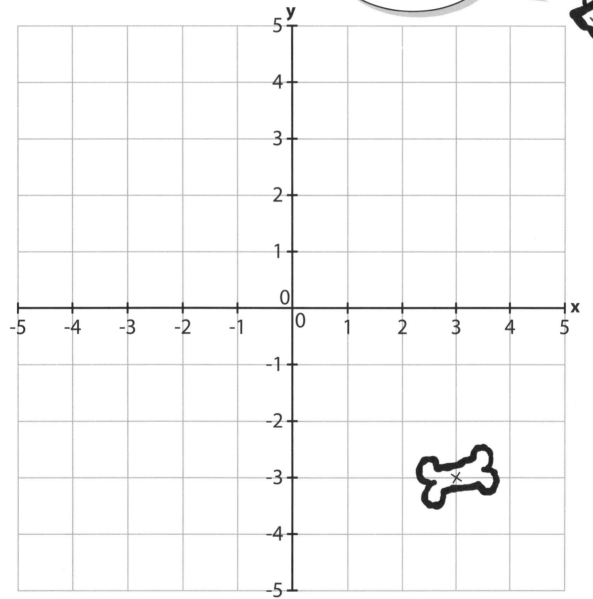

long multiplication

Here are two methods of doing long multiplication.

For example:

```
    H  T  U
    2  4  2
x      1  3
-------------
2  4  2  0  (x10)

   7  2  6  (x3)
-------------
3  1  4  6
```

Grid method:

X	200	40	2	Total
10	2000	400	20	= 2420
3	600	120	6	= 726

=3146

Find the answer to this multiplication using both methods.

```
   H  T  U
   3  1  8
x     2  5
-----------
           (x20)

           (x5)
-----------
```

X	300	10	8	Total
20				=
5				=

=

BOTH METHODS SHOULD HAVE GIVEN YOU THE SAME ANSWER. WHICH DID YOU FIND THE EASIEST?

Find the answers to these multiplications using both methods.

```
  H  T  U
  3  2  6
x    1  2
_____
           (x10)

           (x2)
_____
```

X	300	20	6	Total
10				=
2				=
				=

```
  H  T  U
  4  0  4
x    1  6
_____
           (x10)

           (x6)
_____
```

X	400	0	4	Total
10				=
6				=
				=

```
  H  T  U
  2  1  3
x    2  4
_____
           (x20)

           (x4)
_____
```

X	200	10	3	Total
20				=
4				=
				=

long division

When you divide one number by another number, eg 28 divided by 7, it is like finding out how many 7s there are in 28. The answer is 4 because 4 x 7 = 28.

Look at this example:

```
7 | 2  8  7
```

We know that $28 \div 7 = 4$ so $280 \div 7 = 40$

Then $7 \div 7 = 1$

The answer = 41

We can write it down like this:

```
         4  1
   7 | 2  8  7
     - 2  8  0
              7
```

Now look at this example:

```
          5  0   r 2
   15 | 7  5  2          r = remainder
      - 7  5  0
               2
```

Try these divisions for practice.

get it?

$75 \div 15 = 5$ so $750 \div 15 = 50$.

a. ```20 | 4 8 0```

b. ```22 | 6 6 7```

c. ```14 | 5 7 4```

d. ```50 | 2 6 0```

Always try to estimate your answers first.

For example:

Share £2.04 between 4 children.

You know that £2 ÷ 4 = 50p so you can estimate that
£2.04 ÷ 4 will be a little bit more than 50p.

Now do the division to find out the answer ...

```
        5 1
    4 | 2 0 4
      - 2 0 0
            4    Answer: £2.04 ÷ 4 = 51p
```

Work out these division problems.

Estimate your answers first.

1. Share £5.25 by 5 children.

2. Divide 568 by 8.

3. 901 ÷ 4

4. If Alice can run 5 kilometres per day, how long
would it take her to run 125 kilometres?

5. If Dig eats 156 bones per year, how many
bones does he eat per week?

6. If Kit sleeps 147 hours per week, how many
hours does she sleep per day?

Do you working out here...

Now try dividing some longer numbers! Practise some divisions of your own.

For example:
```
            2 4 1
    12 | 2 8 9 2
       -  2 4
             4 9      28 divided by 12 = 2 r 4
           -   4 8    49 divided by 12 = 4 r 1
                 1 2  12 divided by 12 = 1
```

decimals

A **decimal** is part of a whole number. It is similar to a fraction.

The number before the decimal point is a whole number. The number after the decimal point is a part of a whole number.

Read the decimals on the number line below.

These are tenths of a whole number.

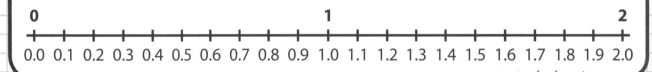

| 0 | | | | | | | | | | 1 | | | | | | | | | | 2 |

0.0 0.1 0.2 0.3 0.4 0.5 0.6 0.7 0.8 0.9 1.0 1.1 1.2 1.3 1.4 1.5 1.6 1.7 1.8 1.9 2.0

Circle the decimal that is bigger in each pair.

a. 0.2 or 2.0

b. 1.2 or 2.1

c. 2.4 or 2.9

d. 3.6 or 0.6

get it?

$0.1 = \frac{1}{10}$

$0.2 = \frac{2}{10}$ (or $\frac{1}{5}$)

$0.3 = \frac{3}{10}$

$0.4 = \frac{4}{10}$ (or $\frac{2}{5}$)

$0.5 = \frac{5}{10}$ (or $\frac{1}{2}$)

Add or subtract these decimals just as you would do with any numbers.

Put the decimal point in your answer.

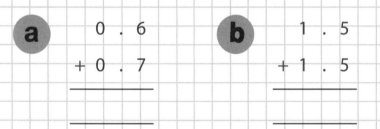

a
```
    0 . 6
  + 0 . 7
  _____

  _____
```

b
```
    1 . 5
  + 1 . 5
  _____

  _____
```

c
```
    2 . 8
  - 1 . 9
  _____

  _____
```

d
```
    3 . 5 0
  - 1 . 7 5
  _____

  _____
```

We use decimals in money.

For example:

1p can be written as 0.01

5p can be written as 0.05

10p can be written as 0.10

50p can be written as 0.50

£1.50 can be written as 1.50

Multiply and divide these decimals.

For example:

```
£   2 . 5 0
x         6
────────────
£ 1 2 . 0 0   (£2 x 6)

£     3 . 0 0   (50p x 6)
────────────
£ 1 5 . 0 0
```

```
      3 . 2 0
  ┌──────────
4 │ £ 1 2 . 8 0
```

a. £2.25 x 4

b. £25.05 ÷ 5

c. £16.20 x 2

d. £28.21 ÷ 7

e. Share £14.40 by 6 children

f. 5 lots of 50p

get it?

Try to estimate your answers first. Make sure you don't forget the decimal point – there is a big difference between £32.40 and £3240!

measures

Learn these equivalents:

1000 grams (g) = 1 kilogram (kg)

1000 millilitres (ml) = 1 litre (l)

1000 metres (m) = 1 kilometre (km)

1000 millimetres (mm) = 1 metre (m)

100 centimetres (cm) = 1 metre (m)

a. Kit can jump 2.5 m. How high is that in centimetres? _____ cm

b. Dig can run 5.4 km without stopping. How far is that in metres? _____ m

c. A quarter of a litre = _____ ml

d. 10 mm = _____ cm

e. Half a kilogram = _____ g

f. 1.50 kg = _____ g

g. 4.9 m = _____ cm

h. 3.2 litres = _____ millilitres

EEK!

get it?

2.5 is the same as 2.50

5.4 is the same as 5.40

3.2 is the same as 3.20

a. Which is more: 1000 ml or 1 litre? _____

b. What is 25 kg as grams? _____ g

c. A fish tank holds 20 litres of water.
How many millilitres is that? _____ ml

d. Dig weighs 10 kg. How much is that in grams? _____ g

e. Kit's bowl holds 250 ml of milk. How many
bowls can be filled from 1 litre of milk? _____ bowls

f. Write 1200 g as kilograms. _____ kg

g. Convert 2.5 cm to millimetres. _____ mm

h. Which is longer: 300 mm or 3 cm? _____

CAT-CH!

moving the decimal

When we multiply a decimal number by 10 we move the decimal point **one** place to the **right**. When we multiply by 100 we move it **two** places. When we multiply by 1000 we move it **three** places.

For example:

4.9 x 10 = 49.00

4.9 x 100 = 490.00

4.9 x 1000 = 4900.00

We can leave out the zeros after the decimal point to simplify the number.

We do the opposite (we move the decimal point to the **left**) when we divide decimal numbers.

For example:

4.9 ÷ 10 = 0.49

4.9 ÷ 100 = 0.049

4.9 ÷ 1000 = 0.0049

Try these:

a. 1.35 x 10 = _____

b. 1.35 x 100 = _____

c. 1.35 x 1000 = _____

d. 1.35 ÷ 10 = _____

e. 1.35 ÷ 100 = _____

f. 1.35 ÷ 1000 = _____

> WHAT'S THE POINT OF DECIMALS?

> I'LL TELL YOU WHAT THE POINT IS! WHICH WOULD YOU RATHER HAVE: £10.50 X 10 OR £0.50 X 1000?

get it?

If you run out of digits use zero as a place holder.

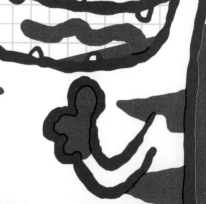

answers

number values
a. fifty-three
b. six hundred and fifty-three
c. one thousand, six hundred and fifty-three
d. twenty-one thousand, six hundred and fifty-three
e. seven hundred and twenty-one thousand, six hundred and fifty-three

a. 2304
b. 9180
c. 11,376
d. 50,604
e. 201,890

a. 4201, 5345, 6032, 7436
b. 5386, 5642, 5740, 5900
c. 6001, 6201, 6389, 6945

decimals
a. 0.01, 0.59, 0.73, 0.90
b. 0.05, 0.09, 0.10, 0.21

negative numbers
-10 -9 -8 -7 -6 -5 -4 -3 -2 -1 0 1 2 3 4 5 6 7 8 9 10

a. -10, -7, -3, -1, 9, 10
b. -7, -2, -1, 4, 7, 9
c. -8, -4, -1, 0, 1, 5

addition and subtraction

add		subtract	
a.	908	a.	289
b.	890	b.	448
c.	3050	c.	563
d.	3627	d.	1094
e.	7299	e.	2502
f.	6510	f.	2829

shapes
symmetry
The parallelogram has no lines of symmetry!

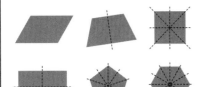

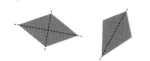

1. True
2. True
3. True
4. True
5. False

Shape	Number of faces	Number of edges	Number of corners (vertices)
Cube	6	12	8
Square-based pyramid	5	8	5
Triangular prism	5	9	6
Cylinder	3	2	0

multiples and factors
count in 3s: 3, 6, 9, 12, 15, 18, 21, 24, 27, 30
count in 4s: 4, 8, 12, 16, 20, 24, 28, 32, 36, 40
count in 6s: 6, 12, 18, 24, 30, 36, 42, 48, 54, 60
count in 8s: 8, 16, 24, 32, 40, 48, 56, 64, 72, 80

multiples of 3: 36, 9, 30, 27, 21
multiples of 6: 36, 30
multiples of 4: 24, 40, 80, 28, 36
multiples of 8: 24, 40, 80

factors of 36	factors of 24
1 x 36	1 x 24
2 x 18	2 x 12
3 x 12	3 x 8
4 x 9	4 x 6
6 x 6	

prime numbers: 11, 5, 13, 7

missing numbers
$3 \times 2 = 6$
$7 \times 7 = 49$
$4 \times 7 = 28$
$15 \times 2 = 30$
$5 \times 7 = 35$

division and multiplication

X	7	5	6	2
3	21	15	18	6
6	42	30	36	12
8	56	40	48	16
4	28	20	24	8

$5 \times 6 = 30$ $5 \times 11 = 55$
$30 \div 6 = 5$ $55 \div 11 = 5$
$30 \div 5 = 6$ $55 \div 5 = 11$

$7 \times 4 = 28$ $8 \times 6 = 48$
$28 \div 4 = 7$ $48 \div 6 = 8$
$28 \div 7 = 4$ $48 \div 8 = 6$

repeated subtraction
$30 \div 5 = [6]$
$30 - 5 - 5 - 5 - 5 - 5 - 5$

$70 \div 10 = [7]$
$70 - 10 - 10 - 10 - 10 - 10 - 10 - 10$

$56 \div 7 = [8]$
$56 - 7 - 7 - 7 - 7 - 7 - 7 - 7 - 7$

subtraction on a number line
$15 \div 3 = [5]$ $15 \rightarrow 12 \rightarrow 9 \rightarrow 6 \rightarrow 3 \rightarrow 0$

$20 \div 5 = [4]$ $20 \rightarrow 15 \rightarrow 10 \rightarrow 5 \rightarrow 0$

perimeter and area
a. $4 + 3 + 5 = 12$ cm
b. $6 + 6 + 3 + 3 = 18$ cm
c. $6 + 6 + 3 + 3 + 3 + 3 = 24$ cm
d. $4 + 4 + 4 + 1 + 2 + 2 + 2 + 1 = 20$ cm

a. 12 cm
b. 15 cm
c. 18 cm

area

a. $15 \times 5 = 75$ cm²
b. $20 \times 8 = 160$ cm²
c. $10 \times 5 = 50$ cm²
   $5 \times 5 = 25$ cm²
   $50 + 25 = 75$ cm²
d. $8 \times 4 = 32$ cm²
   $2 \times 4 = 8$ cm²
   $2 \times 4 = 8$ cm²
   $32 + 8 + 8 = 48$ cm²

area of the rectangle: $3 \times 2 = 6$ cm²
area of the triangle: $6 \div 2 = 3$ cm²

fractions and percentages

a. 8 out of 16 parts = ⁸⁄₁₆ (or ½)
b. 4 out of 16 parts = ⁴⁄₁₆ (or ¼)
c. 3 out of 8 parts = ⅜

a. ⁴⁄₁₀ = ⅖   b. ³⁄₆ = ½   c. ⁸⁄₁₆ = ½
d. ⁴⁄₁₆ = ¼   e. ⁵⁄₁₀ = ½   f. ²⁄₁₀ = ⅕
g. ³⁄₁₂ = ¼   h. ⁴⁄₁₂ = ⅓

a. ½ of 50 = 25   b. 50% of 30 = 15
c. ¼ of 4 = 1   d. 25% of 8 = 2
e. ⅕ of £2.50 = 50p   f. 20% of £5 = £1
g. ⅖ of 25p = 10p   h. 40% of 30p = 12p
i. 10% of £4 = 40p   j. ¹⁄₁₀ of £8 = 80p

fractions

⁹⁄₁₂ (or ¾) is coloured
¾ (or ⁹⁄₁₂) is bigger than ⅔ (or ⁸⁄₁₂)

a. ⅝ is bigger than ¼
b. ¾ is bigger than ⅜
c. ⁴⁄₆ is bigger than ⁴⁄₁₂
d. ⅔ (or ⁸⁄₁₂) is bigger than ⁵⁄₁₂
e. ⁴⁄₆ (or ⅔) is bigger than ⅓

number line fractions

⁴⁄₆ = ⅔
³⁄₁₂ = ¼
³⁄₉ = ⅓
²⁄₄ = ½

smallest to biggest fraction: ¼, ⁴⁄₁₀, ½, ¾

angles and triangles

a. 90°, 45°, 45°   a. reflex   a. 45°, 315°
b. 80°, 35°, 65°   b. acute   b. 180°, 180°
c. 30°, 30°, 120°   c. obtuse   c. 90°, 270°
d. 60°, 60°, 60°   d. right-angle   d. 270°, 90°

coordinates

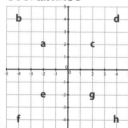
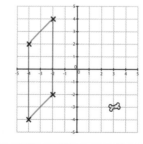

The coordinates for the bone are: [3, -3].
The coordinates [-4, -4] [-4, 2] [-2, 4] [-2, -2] form a parallelogram.

long multiplication

	H T U
	3 1 8
x	2 5
6 3 6 0	(x20)
1 5 9 0	(x5)
7 9 5 0	

X	300	10	8	Total
20	6000	200	160	= 6360
5	1500	50	40	=1590
				=7950

	H T U
	3 2 6
x	1 2
3 2 6 0	(x10)
6 5 2	(x2)
3 9 1 2	

X	300	20	6	Total
10	3000	200	60	= 3260
2	600	40	12	= 652
				=3912

	H T U
	4 0 4
x	1 6
4 0 4 0	(x10)
2 4 2 4	(x6)
6 4 6 4	

X	400	0	4	Total
10	4000	0	40	= 4040
6	2400	0	24	=2424
				=6464

	H T U
	2 1 3
x	2 4
4 2 6 0	(x20)
8 5 2	(x4)
5 1 1 2	

X	200	10	3	Total
20	4000	200	60	= 4260
4	800	40	12	= 852
				=5112

long division

a. 24   1. £1.05 each   5. 3 bones
b. 30 r 7   2. 71   per week
c. 41   3. 225 r 1   6. 21 hours
d. 5 r 10   4. 25 days   per day

decimals

a. 2.0   a. 1.3   a. £2.25 × 4 = £9.00   e. £14.40 ÷ 6 = £2.40
b. 2.1   b. 3.0   b. £25.05 ÷ 5 = £5.01   f. 5 × 50p = £2.50
c. 2.9   c. 0.9   c. £16.20 × 2 = £32.40
d. 3.6   d. 1.75   d. £28.21 ÷ 7 = £4.03

measures

a. 2.5 m = 250 cm   a. 1000 ml and 1 litre are
b. 5.4 km = 5,400 m   the same.
c. 1000 ml ÷ 4 = 250 ml   b. 25 kg = 25,000 g
d. 10 mm = 1 cm   c. 20 litres = 20,000 ml
e. 1000 g ÷ 2 = 500 g   d. 10 kg = 10,000 g
f. 1.50 kg = 1,500 g   e. 1000 ml ÷ 250 ml = 4 (bowls)
g. 4.9 m = 490 cm   f. 1200 g = 1.2 kg
h. 3.2 litres = 3,200 millilitres g. 2.5 cm = 25 mm
                                  h. 300 mm (or 30 cm) is longer
moving the decimal   than 3 cm

a. 1.35 × 10 = 13.5
b. 1.35 × 100 = 135
c. 1.35 × 1000 = 1350
d. 1.35 ÷ 10 = 0.135
e. 1.35 ÷ 100 = 0.0135
f. 1.35 ÷ 1000 = 0.00135

notes, practice and workings out

Maths revision

SO HOW DID YOU GET ON?

READY FOR MORE?!

LET'S REVISE SOME OF THE THINGS YOU'VE BEEN LEARNING ABOUT. REMEMBER, PRACTICE MAKES PERFECT!

YOU'LL FIND THE ANSWERS AT THE END OF THIS SECTION. THERE ARE LOTS OF EXTRA PAGES FOR PRACTICE AND FOR SHOWING YOUR WORKINGS OUT. TRY TO WORK THROUGH THE SECTION IN PAGE ORDER AND TAKE BREAKS WHEN YOU NEED THEM. *GOOD LUCK!*

number values

Each digit in a number has a **value**.

For example:
3450 = 3000 + 400 + 50 + 0

Remember:
9999 = 9000 + 900 + 90 + 9

Write the missing number values in the boxes.

a. 4098 = [ ] + [ ] + [90] + [ ]   **b.** 5667 [5000] [ ] [ ] [ ]

c. 3824 = [ ] + [800] + [ ] + [ ]   **d.** 1951 = [ ] + [ ] + [ ] + [1]

Find out:

a. Which is more: 5 hundreds or 55 tens? _____

b. Which is less: 6 thousands or 61 hundreds? _____

c. What is the biggest number you can make with these digits: 2948? _____

d. What is the difference between: 98,430 and 97,430? _____

e. What do you need to add to 76,305 to make 76,605? _____

Write these numbers in figures.

a. Nine thousand, eight hundred and eight = _____

b. Eight thousand, six hundred and forty-two = _____

c. Three thousand, seven hundred and ninety-nine = _____

Work out the following:

a. 4590 ...+... 10 more is _____4600_____

b. 8934 .... 10 less is _____

c. 3193 .... 100 more is _____

d. 6176 .... 100 less is _____

e. 8321 .... 1000 more is _____

f. 5869 .... 1000 less is _____

Check out these numbers:

5000	five thousand
500	five hundred
50	fifty
5	five
0.5	nought point five
0.05	nought point nought five

Write these numbers in order from the smallest to the biggest.

Watch out for the decimals!

a. 5630, 521, 0.56, 5780, 540

_____ _____ _____ _____ _____

b. 6900, 0.06, 634, 691, 6999

_____ _____ _____ _____ _____

c. 0.70, 7809, 750, 0.07, 7001

_____ _____ _____ _____ _____

d. 8003, 0.83, 0.08, 855, 8300

_____ _____ _____ _____ _____

45

addition and subtraction

Add these numbers in your head:

$40 + 50 + 60 =$ _____ $20 + 70 + 10 =$ _____

$25 + 25 + 70 =$ _____ $50 + 25 + 30 =$ _____

When adding bigger numbers it is easier to use a written method.

For example:

```
      Th H  T  U
          1  8  6  7
      +      2  3  5
      ─────────────
          2  1  0  2
            1  1  1
```

remember:

Add the units first. Carry over any tens to the tens column, hundreds to the hundreds column and thousands to the thousands column.

Add these numbers.

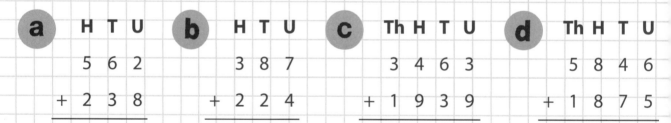

a
```
  H  T  U
  5  6  2
+ 2  3  8
─────────
```

b
```
  H  T  U
  3  8  7
+ 2  2  4
─────────
```

c
```
Th H  T  U
   3  4  6  3
+  1  9  3  9
────────────
```

d
```
Th H  T  U
   5  8  4  6
+  1  8  7  5
────────────
```

e Find the total of
$460 + 13 + 7 + 3402$

```
Th  H  T  U



+
───────────

```

f Find the total of
$55 + 9 + 342 + 1348$

```
Th  H  T  U



+
───────────

```

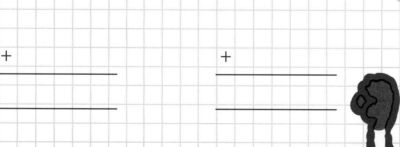

MAKE SURE THE NUMBERS ARE IN THE CORRECT COLUMNS.

Try these subtractions.

For example:

```
     Th  H   T   U
      0  13  11  1
      X̶   4̶   2̶   3
  –          7   6   5
  ─────────────────────
             6   5   8
```

remember:

Subtract the units first. Exchange (or borrow) from other columns if you need to, eg a ten for 10 units, a hundred for 10 tens and a thousand for 10 hundreds.

Subtract these numbers.

a
```
      H   T   U
      4   6   3
  –   1   3   9
  ─────────────
```

b
```
      H   T   U
      2   3   5
  –   1   4   9
  ─────────────
```

c
```
  Th  H   T   U
   2  3   6   4
  – 1  8   5   7
  ─────────────────
```

d
```
  Th  H   T   U
   4  5   2   1
  – 1  8   7   5
  ─────────────────
```

e
```
  Th  H   T   U
   3  7   6   5
  – 1  9   7   5
  ─────────────────
```

f
```
  Th  H   T   U
   5  3   4   2
  – 1  6   9   5
  ─────────────────
```

decimals

A **decimal** is part of a whole number. It is similar to a fraction.

0.5 is the same as ½

1.5 is the same as 1½

We say:

0.5 = nought point five

1.5 = one point five

Write these decimals on the number line.

0.2   0.5   1.3   1.5   1.9   0.7   1.1   0.8

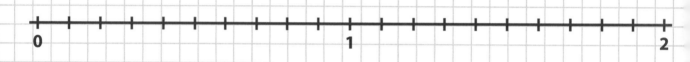

0   1   2

Write these numbers in order from the smallest to the biggest.

a. 7.3, 6.5, 9.2, 5.1

_____   _____   _____   _____

b. 96p, £1.06, £96, £1.96

_____   _____   _____   _____

c. 0.5 cm, 1.5 cm, 2.5 cm, 1.2 cm

_____   _____   _____   _____

d. 5.2 m, 5.5 m, 5.1 m, 5.9 m

_____   _____   _____   _____

MONEY IS WRITTEN IN DECIMALS – SO IT'S WORTH YOUR WHILE GETTING TO KNOW THEM!

Money and other measures, such as length, weight and volume, use decimals.

For example:

100 cm = 1 m	1000 g = 1 kg	1000 ml = 1 litre
150 cm = 1.5 m	1100 g = 1.1 kg	1900 ml = 1.9 litres

Find out:

a. How many pence in £2.50? _____ p

b. What is 673p in pounds and pence? £ _____

c. How many centimetres in 1.10 metres? _____ cm

d. What is 350 cm written in metres? _____ m

e. What comes next? 5.0, 5.2, 5.4, _____ , _____

f. What comes next? 7.1, 6.9, 6.7, _____ , _____

g. What is 1400 g in kilograms? _____ kg

h. How many millilitres in 1.4 litres? _____ml

Decimals have fraction equivalents.

For example:

$$0.50 = \frac{1}{2} \quad 0.25 = \frac{1}{4} \quad 0.20 = \frac{1}{5} \quad 0.1 = \frac{1}{10} \quad 0.01 = \frac{1}{100}$$

PUT THESE FRACTIONS IN A CALCULATOR TO CHECK THE DECIMAL EQUIVALENTS.

remember:

0.50 is the same as 0.5

In money, 0.5 would be worth 50p.

0.05 would be 5p.

Draw a line to join each decimal to its fraction equivalent.

0.20	0.02	0.60	0.75	0.35	0.10
$\frac{75}{100}$	$\frac{35}{100}$	$\frac{20}{100}$	$\frac{2}{100}$	$\frac{10}{100}$	$\frac{60}{100}$

Look for the pattern when you multiply by 10:

5 x 10 = 50

50 x 10 = 500

500 x 10 = 5000

Look for the pattern when you divide by 10:

50 ÷ 10 = 5

500 ÷ 10 = 50

5000 ÷ 10 = 500

Find out:

a. What is 6 x 10? _____

b. What is 15 x 10? _____

c. What is 330 x 10? _____

d. What is 70 ÷ 10? _____

e. What is 200 ÷ 10? _____

f. What is 4000 ÷ 10? _____

Solve these problems.

a. Each packet contains 10 biscuits. There are 15 packets in a carton.
How many biscuits are in the carton?

_____ biscuits

b. Dog food costs 80p per tin. Dig wants to buy 10 tins. How much money does he need?

£_____

c. A basic dog collar costs £3. A diamante dog collar costs ten times as much.
How much is the diamante dog collar?

£_____

d. If a dog drinks 1.5 litres of water a day, how much will 10 dogs drink?

_____ litres

remember:

1.5 litres is 1500 millilitres.

Look for the pattern when you multiply by 100:

5 x 100 = 500

50 x 100 = 5000

500 x 100 = 50,000

Look for the pattern when you divide by 100:

500 ÷ 100 = 5

5000 ÷ 100 = 50

50,000 ÷ 100 = 500

Find out:

a. What is 3 x 100? _____

b. What is 25 x 100? _____

c. What is 410 x 100? _____

d. What is 200 ÷100? _____

e. What is 1000 ÷ 100? _____

f. What is 2000 ÷ 100? _____

Calculate the following:

a. One-tenth of 120 is _____

b. One-hundredth of 700 is _____

c. Two-tenths of 60 is _____

d. Two-hundredths of 800 is _____

e. Five-tenths (or ½) of £1.50 is _____

f. Five-hundredths of £1 is _____

WHICH WOULD YOU PREFER? ONE-HUNDREDTH OF £100 OR FIVE-TENTHS OF £20?

remember:
To find **one-tenth (1/10)** of something we **divide by 10.** To find **one-hundredth (1/100)** of something we **divide by 100.**

number sequences

Count in 3s to 30

_____

Count in 6s to 60

_____

Count in 9s to 90

WHAT DO YOU NOTICE ABOUT THE 3s, 6s AND 9s SEQUENCES?

_____

Count in 2s to 20

_____

Count in 4s to 40

_____

Count in 8s to 80

WHAT DO YOU NOTICE ABOUT THE 2s, 4s AND 8s SEQUENCES?

_____

Count in 5s to 50

_____

Count in 10s to 100

WHAT DO YOU NOTICE ABOUT THE 5s AND 10s SEQUENCES?

_____

Count in 25s to 250

_____

Count in 50s to 500

WHAT DO YOU NOTICE ABOUT THE 25s AND 50s SEQUENCES?

_____

Count on from 11 in 5s

_____

Count back from 53 in 5s

_____

Count on from 10 in 9s

_____

Count back from 88 in 9s

_____

Complete this multiplication square. Then colour in the multiples of 3. What do you notice?

1	2	3	4	5	6	7	8	9	10
2	4	6	8	10		14	16		
3	6		12		18	21		27	
4		12	16	20		28	32	36	40
5		15	20					45	50
6				30	36	42	48		
7		21						63	70
8	16			40	48	56			
9	18	27	36	45	54		72	81	90
10	20	30	40	50	60	70	80	90	

remember:
Subtracting 9 is easier if you subtract 10 first, then add 1.

Complete this multiplication square. Then colour in the multiples of 4. What do you notice?

1	2	3	4	5	6	7	8	9	10
2		6	8	10		14			
3	6		12			21	24	27	
4	8							36	40
5		15	20	25	30		40		
6			24					54	60
7	14			35	42	49	56		
8					48		64	72	80
9	18	27	36	45					90
10	20	30	40			70	80	90	

fractions

A **fraction** is a part of a whole.

If we halve something, we divide it into two equal parts.

We write this as: $\frac{1}{2}$

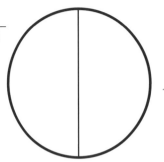

Colour these fractions of the shapes.

1 Colour $\frac{1}{2}$

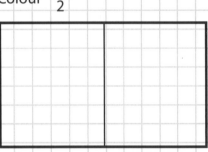

2 Colour $\frac{2}{3}$

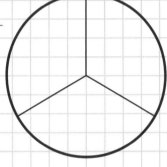

3 Colour $\frac{2}{4}$

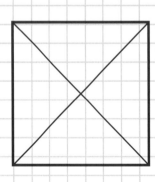

4 Colour $\frac{4}{5}$

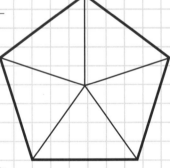

5 Colour $\frac{3}{6}$

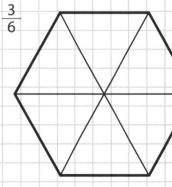

$\frac{2}{4}$ AND $\frac{3}{6}$ ARE THE SAME AS $\frac{1}{2}$!!

Fractions that have the same value are called **equivalent fractions**.

For example:

$\frac{1}{2}$ is the same as $\frac{4}{8}$, $\frac{5}{10}$, $\frac{6}{12}$ and $\frac{50}{100}$ etc.

Can you think of any other equivalent fractions? Write them in the space below.

Draw a ring around the fractions that are less than $\frac{1}{2}$.

$\frac{6}{14}$ $\frac{3}{8}$ $\frac{5}{10}$ $\frac{9}{20}$ $\frac{60}{100}$ $\frac{7}{16}$ $\frac{9}{12}$

Draw a ring around the fractions that are more than $\frac{1}{2}$.

$\frac{12}{20}$ $\frac{7}{12}$ $\frac{4}{8}$ $\frac{9}{16}$ $\frac{6}{18}$ $\frac{6}{10}$ $\frac{8}{24}$

Write these fractions in order from the smallest.

$\frac{1}{5}$ $\frac{3}{4}$ $\frac{1}{10}$ $\frac{3}{6}$

___   ___   ___   ___

remember:
You can simplify a fraction by dividing the top number and the bottom number by the same factor.

eg $\frac{12}{16}$ (÷ by 4) = $\frac{3}{4}$

What fraction of this shape is coloured?

shapes

Name these shapes.

a

b

c

_____ _____ _____

d

e

_____

_____ _____

Complete the following statement.

A cube has:

_____ faces.

_____ edges.

_____ corners (vertices).

edge

corner

face

face

56

Write true (T) or false (F) next to each of these statements.

1. A triangle has 3 sides. ☐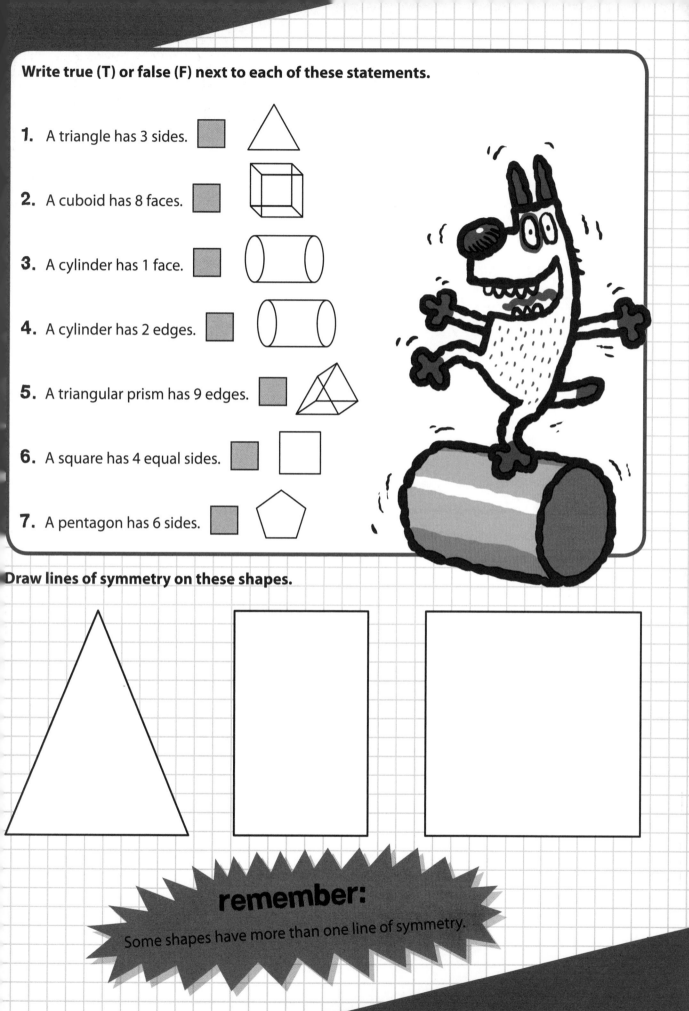

2. A cuboid has 8 faces. ☐

3. A cylinder has 1 face. ☐

4. A cylinder has 2 edges. ☐

5. A triangular prism has 9 edges. ☐

6. A square has 4 equal sides. ☐

7. A pentagon has 6 sides. ☐

Draw lines of symmetry on these shapes.

remember:
Some shapes have more than one line of symmetry.

angles

An **angle** is a rotation around a point. We measure angles in **degrees** using a protractor.

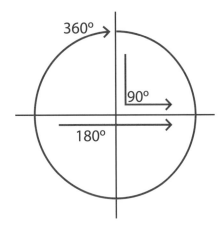

360 degrees = a circle

180 degrees = a straight line

90 degrees = a quarter-turn (a right angle)

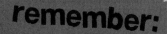
An angle **less** than 90 degrees is called **acute**.

An angle **more** than 90 degrees is called **obtuse**.

Label these angles 'acute' or 'obtuse'.

a _____

b _____

c _____

d _____

Calculate the unknown angle.

a **?** 45° _____

b **?** 90° _____

c **?** 30° _____

d **?** 135° _____

The angles in a triangle add up to 180 degrees.

60°
60° 60°

remember:
If you know two of the angles in a triangle you can calculate the third angle by subtracting from 180.

a
?
70° 70°
_____

b
?
60° 60°
_____

c
?
45° 90°
_____

d
?
100° 40°
_____

There are different types of triangle:

equilateral – 3 equal sides, 3 equal angles

isosceles – 2 equal sides, 2 equal angles

scalene – no equal sides, no equal angles

right-angled – one right angle

Identify these triangles using the definitions above.

a

_____

b

_____

c

_____

d

_____

remember:
A right-angle triangle is labelled like this:

multiplication

Multiply the numbers below using the following method.

For example: 56 x 7 = (50 x 7) + (6 x 7)

= 350 + 42

= **392**

Now it's your turn!

a 43 x 5 = (_____) + (_____)

= _____ + _____

= _____

b 28 x 3 = (_____) + (_____)

= _____ + _____

= _____

c 36 x 4 = (_____) + (_____)

= _____ + _____

= _____

d 69 x 10 = (_____) + (_____)

= _____ + _____

= _____

Multiply the numbers below using the grid method.

For example: **52 x 36**

X	50	2	Total
30	1500	60	= 1560
6	300	12	= 312
			= **1872**

Give it a go!

a 27 x 34

X			Total
			=
			=
			=

b 41 x 16

X			Total
			=
			=
			=

Find the answers to these long multiplications using the following methods.

For example:

```
        1  4  2
    x      2  6
   ─────────────
    2  8  4  0   (x20)
       8  5  2   (x6)
   ─────────────
    3  6  9  2
```

X	100	40	2	Total
20	2000	800	40	= 2840
6	600	240	12	= 852
				= **3692**

a

```
        2  3  5
    x      2  5
   ─────────────
                 (x20)

                 (x5)
   ─────────────
```

X				Total
				=
				=
				=

b

```
        4  1  6
    x      2  7
   ─────────────
                 (x20)

                 (x7)
   ─────────────
```

X				Total
				=
				=
				=

c

```
        3  0  8
    x      2  4
   ─────────────
                 (x20)

                 (x4)
   ─────────────
```

X				Total
				=
				=
				=

d

```
        2  3  2
    x      3  2
   ─────────────
                 (x30)

                 (x2)
   ─────────────
```

X				Total
				=
				=
				=

division

Division is the opposite of multiplication.

For example:

$7 \times 6 = 42$ **So...** $42 \div 7 = 6$ and $42 \div 6 = 7$

Write two division facts for each multiplication below.

a. $8 \times 10 =$ _____

_____

_____

b. $80 \times 10 =$ _____

_____

_____

c. $50 \times 5 =$ _____

_____

_____

d. $500 \times 5 =$ _____

_____

_____

Dividing long numbers in your head is difficult so you need to learn a written method.

For example:

```
           3   4  r1
      6 | 2  0  5
      -   1  8      (6 x 3)
           2  5
      -    2  4      (6 x 4)
              1
```

'R' MEANS REMAINDER!

remember:
Division is also like repeated subtraction.
E.g. $42 \div 6 = 42 - 6 - 6 - 6 - 6 - 6 - 6 - 6$

a

$5 | 4 \ 5 \ 7$

b

$3 | 6 \ 0 \ 4$

c

$2 | 1 \ 5 \ 6$

d

$8 | 3 \ 4 \ 7$

e

$4 | 5 \ 2 \ 0$

Always try to estimate your answers first when you are dividing.

For example: **300 ÷ 9**

You know that 300 ÷ 10 = 30 so you can estimate that 300 ÷ 9 will be a bit more than 30.

Now do the division to find out the answer …

```
        3  3 r 3
   9 │ 3  0  0
     -  2  7    (3 x 9)
           3  0
     -     2  7  (3 x 9)
              3
```

Work out these division problems.

Estimate your answers first.

1. Share £11.50 equally between Dig and Kit.

2. 720 divide by 3.

3. How many 150 cm dog leads can you make from 600 cm?

4. 696 ÷ 6

5. Share 2060 by 20.

6. How many groups of 8 are there in 448?

Do your working out here...

Rounding numbers

When making rough estimates in your head, rounding numbers (up or down) is useful.

For example, numbers from 101 to 104 can be rounded down to 100 and from 105 to 109 rounded up to 110.

Round these numbers to the nearest ten.

a. 21 _____   **b.** 687 _____

c. 453 _____   **d.** 999 _____

area and perimeter

Area is a measurement of the space inside a shape.

If each square represents 1 square cm, what area is shaded?

_____ cm²

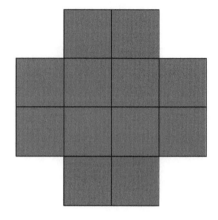

Perimeter is the distance around the edges of a shape.

What is the perimeter of the shape above? _____ cm

Draw your own shape in this space and find out its perimeter and area.

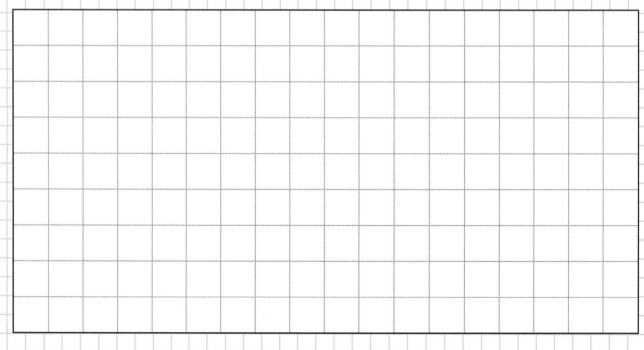

Find the area and perimeter of these shapes.

For example:

6 cm

2 cm area = 2 x 6 = 12 cm²

perimeter = 2 + 2 + 6 + 6 = 16 cm

a **14 cm**

10 cm

area = _____ cm²

perimeter = _____ cm

b **20 cm**

4 cm

area = _____ cm²

perimeter = _____ cm

c **15 cm**

7 cm

area = _____ cm²

perimeter = _____ cm

d **10 cm**

30 cm

area = _____ cm²

perimeter = _____ cm

What is the approximate area of this rectangle?

Round the decimals down or up to find out.

12.4 cm

19.7 cm

area = _____ cm²

65

coordinates

Coordinates are the numbers we use to pinpoint a place on a graph or map.

Look at the map below. You will find Skull Rock at (4, 5). Write the coordinates for the following:

a. Creepy cave (__ , __)

b. Stinky swamp (__ , __)

c. Skull and crossbones (__ , __)

d. Buried treasure (__ , __)

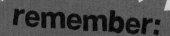

remember:
First you read along the x axis, then the y axis.

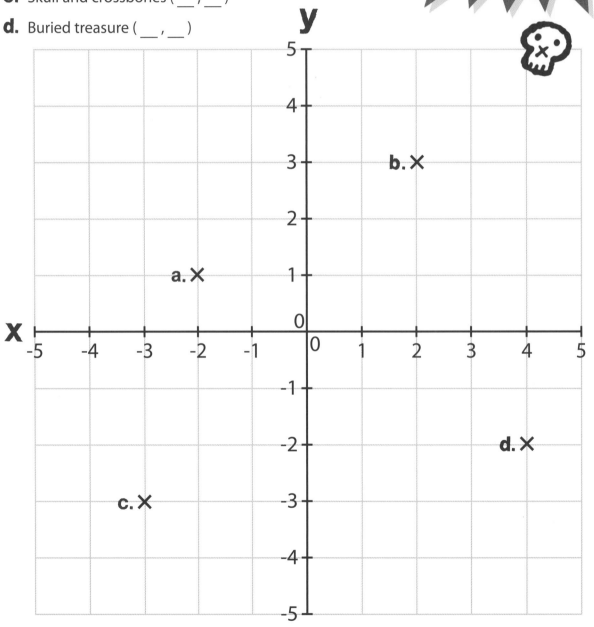

Draw your own treasure map with buried treasure.

Write the coordinates of the buried treasure here: (__ , __)

Write the coordinates for three other important places on your map.

Place name: _____ (__ , __)

Place name: _____ (__ , __)

Place name: _____ (__ , __)

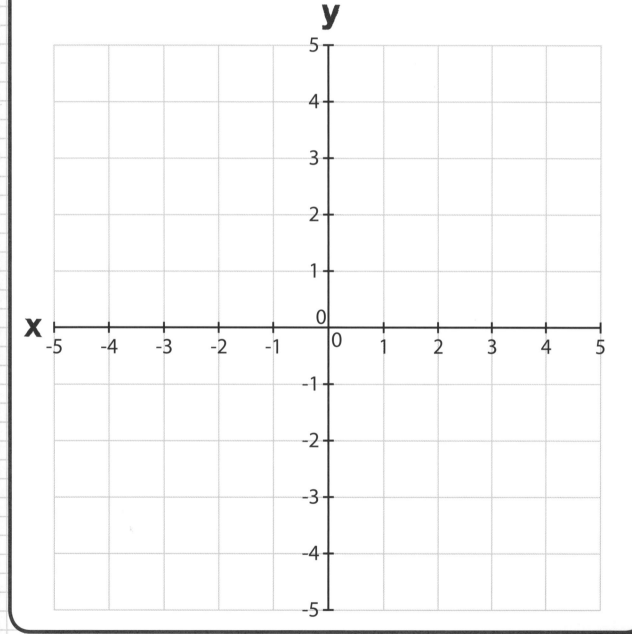

negative numbers

Complete this temperature scale.

$$\boxed{-\ \ -9\ \ -\ \ -\ \ -6\ -5\ -4\ \ -\ \ -2\ -1\ 0\ 1\ 2\ 3\ 4\ 5\ 6\ 7\ 8\ 9\ 10}$$

Use the number line to do these subtractions by counting back.

a. $-4 - 6 =$ _____

b. $-3 - 5 =$ _____

c. $-1 - 4 =$ _____

d. $6 - 8 =$ _____

e. $2 - 5 =$ _____

remember:

$-4 - 3 = -7$

But $4 - 3 = 1$

BRRR! IT'S FREEZING IN HERE.

YOU ARE SO NEGATIVE!

percentages

A **percentage** is a part of a hundred.

Revise these percentage and fraction equivalents:

$1\% = \dfrac{1}{100}$ (one hundredth)

$10\% = \dfrac{10}{100}$ (one-tenth)

$25\% = \dfrac{25}{100}$ (one quarter)

$50\% = \dfrac{50}{100}$ (half)

What percentage of each shape is shaded?

 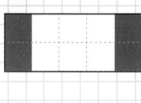

Now try these!

a. 50% of 100 = _____

b. 50% of 40 = _____

c. 25% of £1 = _____p

d. 10% of £1 = _____p

e. 10% of 50p = _____p

f. $\dfrac{1}{4}$ of 80 cm = _____cm

g. 25% of 1 kg = _____g

h. $\dfrac{1}{10}$ of 30 ml = _____ml

Colour in 75% of each shape.

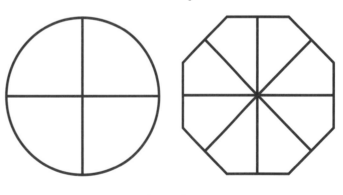

remember:

$75\% = 50\% + 25\%$ or $\dfrac{1}{2} + \dfrac{1}{4}$

graphs

Look at the bar graph that shows the height of children in Class 6.

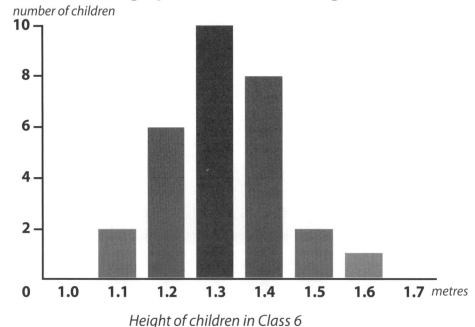

number of children

Height of children in Class 6

Answer the following questions based on the graph.

a. What height are most children in Class 6? _____m

b. What is 1.2 m in centimetres? _____cm

c. What height are the shortest children in the class? _____cm

d. What is the difference in height between the shortest and the tallest child? _____cm

e. How many children are in Class 6? _____ children

WHO'S TALLER?

Look at the pie chart that shows the children's eye colours in Class 7.

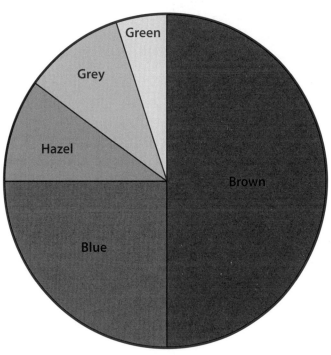

Eye colour of children in Class 7

There are 20 children in Class 7.

Answer the following questions based on the pie chart.

a. Which is the most common eye colour? _____

b. Which is the least common eye colour? _____

c. How many children have grey eyes? _____

d. What percentage of children have brown eyes? _____%

e. What percentage of children have blue eyes? _____%

LOOK INTO MY EYES!

puzzles

1. Count all the squares you can find in this shape.

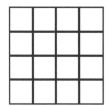

2. Complete this number sudoku so that each 3 x 2 block includes all the numbers from 1 to 6. The columns and rows must also include all these numbers.

3				1	4
	1	6			
	6	4	5		3
		2	4	6	1
6			3		
2	5				6

3. Complete these multiplication tables.

X	7	4	2	Total
3	21			= 39
	42			=
		32		=
5				=

X	6		9	Total
	36			=
7		70		=
			27	=
	30			=

4. Write the factors for each number on these spider diagrams.

a

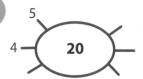

5
4

20

b

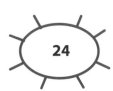

24

c

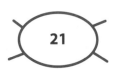

21

d

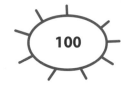

100

5. A short dog lead is 100 cm long. A long lead is 2 m. How much longer is the long lead in centimetres? _____ cm

answers

number values
a. 4098 = 4000 + 0 + 90 + 8
b. 5667 = 5000 + 600 + 60 + 7
c. 3824 = 3000 + 800 + 20 + 4
d. 1951 = 1000 + 900 + 50 + 1

a. 55 tens is more
b. 6 thousands is less
c. 9842
d. 1000
e. 300

a. 9808
b. 8642
c. 3799

a. 4590 + 10 = 4600
b. 8934 – 10 = 8924
c. 3193 + 100 = 3293
d. 6176 – 100 = 6076
e. 8321 + 1000 = 9321
f. 5869 – 1000 = 4869

a. 0.56, 521, 540, 5630, 5780
b. 0.06, 634, 691, 6900, 6999
c. 0.07, 0.70, 750, 7001, 7809
d. 0.08, 0.83, 855, 8003, 8300

addition and subtraction
40 + 50 + 60 = 150
20 + 70 + 10 = 100
25 + 25 + 70 = 120
50 + 25 + 30 = 105

a. 800   **a.** 324
b. 611   **b.** 86
c. 5402   **c.** 507
d. 7721   **d.** 2646
e. 3882   **e.** 1790
f. 1754   **f.** 3647

decimals

0   0.2   0.5   0.7 0.8   1   1.1   1.3   1.5   1.9   2

a. 5.1, 6.5, 7.3, 9.2
b. 96p, £1.06, £1.96, £96
c. 0.5 cm, 1.2 cm, 1.5 cm, 2.5 cm
d. 5.1 m, 5.2 m, 5.5 m, 5.9 m

a. 250p
b. £6.73
c. 110 cm
d. 3.5 m
e. 5.0, 5.2, 5.4, 5.6, 5.8
f. 7.1, 6.9, 6.7, 6.5, 6.3
g. 1.4 kg
h. 1400 ml

0.20 = 20/100
0.02 = 2/100
0.60 = 60/100
0.75 = 75/100

0.35 = 35/100
0.10 = 10/100

x and ÷ 10 and 100
a. 60
b. 150
c. 3300
d. 7
e. 20
f. 400

a. 150 biscuits
b. £8
c. £30
d. 15 litres

a. 300
b. 2500
c. 41 000
d. 2
e. 10
f. 20

a. One-tenth of 120 is 12
b. One-hundredth of 700 is 7
c. Two-tenths of 60 is 12
d. Two-hundredths of 800 is 16
e. Five-tenths (or ½) of £1.50 is 75p
f. Five-hundredths of £1 is 5p

number sequences
3s: 3, 6, 9, 12, 15, 18, 21, 24, 27, 30
6s: 6, 12, 18, 24, 30, 36, 42, 48, 54, 60
9s: 9, 18, 27, 36, 45, 54, 63, 72, 81, 90

The 3s sequence is double the 6s.
The 9s sequence is the 6s plus the 3s.

2s: 2, 4, 6, 8, 10, 12, 14, 16, 18, 20
4s: 4, 8, 12, 16, 20, 24, 28, 32, 36, 40
8s: 8, 16, 24, 32, 40, 48, 56, 64, 72, 80

The 4s sequence is double the 2s.
The 8s sequence is the 4s plus the 2s.

5s: 5, 10, 15, 20, 25, 30, 35, 40, 45, 50
10s: 10, 20, 30, 40, 50, 60, 70, 80, 90, 100

The 10s sequence is double the 5s.

25s: 25, 50, 75, 100, 125, 150, 175, 200, 225, 250
50s: 50, 100, 150, 200, 250, 300, 350, 400, 450, 500

The 50s sequence is double the 25s.

11, 16, 21, 26, 31, 36, 41, 46, 51 and so on...
53, 48, 43, 38, 33, 28, 23, 18, 13, 8, 3
10, 19, 28, 37, 46, 55, 64, 73, 82, 91 and so on...
88, 79, 70, 61, 52, 43, 34, 25, 16, 7

Multiples of 3

1	2	3	4	5	6	7	8	9	10
2	4	6	8	10	12	14	16	18	20
3	6	9	12	15	18	21	24	27	30
4	8	12	16	20	24	28	32	36	40
5	10	15	20	25	30	35	40	45	50
6	12	18	24	30	36	42	48	54	60
7	14	21	28	35	42	49	56	63	70
8	16	24	32	40	48	56	64	72	80
9	18	27	36	45	54	63	72	81	90
10	20	30	40	50	60	70	80	90	100

Multiples of 4

1	2	3	4	5	6	7	8	9	10
2	4	6	8	10	12	14	16	18	20
3	6	9	12	15	18	21	24	27	30
4	8	12	16	20	24	28	32	36	40
5	10	15	20	25	30	35	40	45	50
6	12	18	24	30	36	42	48	54	60
7	14	21	28	35	42	49	56	63	70
8	16	24	32	40	48	56	64	72	80
9	18	27	36	45	54	63	72	81	90
10	20	30	40	50	60	70	80	90	100

fractions
1.

2.

3.

4.

5.

These fractions are less than ½:
⁶⁄₁₄   ³⁄₈   ⁹⁄₂₀   ⁷⁄₁₆

These fractions are more than ½:
¹²⁄₂₀   ⁷⁄₁₂   ⁹⁄₁₆   ⁶⁄₁₀

These fractions are in order from the smallest: ¹⁄₁₀ ⅓ ³⁄₆ ¾

¹²⁄₁₆ (or ⅚ or ¾) of the shape is coloured.

shapes
a. rectangle
b. (regular) hexagon
c. square-based pyramid
d. cylinder
e. (triangular) prism

A cube has:
6 faces
12 edges
8 corners (vertices)

1. True: a triangle has 3 sides.
2. False: because a cuboid has 6 faces.
3. False: because a cylinder has 3 faces.
4. True: a cylinder has 2 edges.
5. True: a triangular prism has 9 edges.
6. True: a square has 4 equal sides.
7. False: because a pentagon has 5 sides.

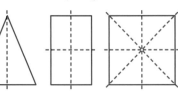

angles
a. obtuse
b. acute
c. acute
d. obtuse

a. 135°
b. 90°
c. 150°
d. 45°

a. 40°
b. 60°
c. 45°
d. 40°

a. isosceles
b. scalene
c. right-angled
d. equilateral

multiplication
a. 43 x 5 = (40 x 5) + (3 x 5)
= 200 + 15
= 215

b. 28 x 3 = (20 x 3) + (8 x 3)
= 60 + 24
= 84

c. 36 x 4 = (30 x 4) + (6 x 4)
= 120 + 24
= 144

d. 69 x 10 = (60 x 10) + (9 x 10)
= 600 + 90
= 690

---

a. 27 x 34

X	20	7	Total
30	600	210	= 810
4	80	28	= 108
			= 918

b. 41 x 16

X	40	1	Total
10	400	10	= 410
6	240	6	= 246
			= 656

a.
```
    2 3 5
x     2 5
4 7 0 0 (x20)
1 1 7 5 (x5)
5 8 7 5
```

X	200	30	5	Total
20	4000	600	100	=4700
5	1000	150	25	=1175
				=5875

b.
```
    4 1 6
x     2 7
8 3 2 0 (x20)
2 9 1 2 (x7)
1 1 2 3 2
```

X	400	10	6	Total
20	8000	200	120	=8320
7	2800	70	42	=2912
				=11232

c.
```
    3 0 8
x     2 4
6 1 6 0 (x20)
1 2 3 2 (x4)
7 3 9 2
```

X	300	0	8	Total
20	6000	0	160	=6160
4	1200	0	32	=1232
				=7392

d.
```
    2 3 2
x     3 2
6 9 6 0 (x30)
  4 6 4 (x2)
7 4 2 4
```

X	200	30	2	Total
30	6000	900	60	=6960
2	400	60	4	= 464
				=7424

division
a. 8 x 10 = 80
80 ÷ 10 = 8
80 ÷ 8 = 10

b. 80 x 10 = 800
800 ÷ 10 = 80
800 ÷ 80 = 10

c. 50 x 5 = 250
250 ÷ 5 = 50
250 ÷ 50 = 5

d. 500 x 5 = 2500
2500 ÷ 5 = 500
2500 ÷ 500 = 5

a. 91 r 2
b. 201 r 1
c. 78
d. 43 r 3
e. 130

1. £5.75
2. 240
3. 4 leads
4. 116
5. 103
6. 56 groups

Rounding numbers
a. 20
b. 690
c. 450
d. 1000

area and perimeter
The area of the shape is 12 cm².
The perimeter of the shape is 16 cm.

a. area = 140 cm²   perimeter = 48 cm
b. area = 80 cm²   perimeter = 48 cm
c. area = 105 cm²   perimeter = 44 cm
d. area = 300 cm²   perimeter = 80 cm

The area of the rectangle is approximately
12 x 20 cm = 240 cm²

coordinates
a. (-2, 1)   b. (2, 3)
c. (-3 , -3)   d. (4, -2)

negative numbers
a. - 4 – 6 = -10
b. - 3 – 5 = -8
c. -1 – 4 = -5
d. 6 – 8 = -2
e. 2 – 5 = -3

percentages
a. ¹⁰⁄₂₀ or ½ or 50%
b. ⁴⁄₁₀ or ⅖ or 40%

a. 50% of 100 = 50
b. 50% of 40 = 20
c. 25% of £1 = 25p
d. 10% of £1 = 10p
e. 10% of 50p = 5p
f. ¼ of 80 cm = 20 cm
g. 25% of 1 kg = 250 g
h. ¹⁄₁₀ of 30 ml = 3 ml

graphs
a. 1.3 m
b. 120 cm
c. 110 cm
d. 50 cm
e. 29 children

a. brown
b. green
c. 2 children
d. 50%
e. 25%

puzzles
1. You should find at least 26 squares!

2.

3	2	5	6	1	4
4	1	6	2	3	5
1	6	4	5	2	3
5	3	2	4	6	1
6	4	1	3	5	2
2	5	3	1	4	6

3.

X	7	4	2	Total
3	21	12	6	= 39
6	42	24	12	= 78
8	56	32	16	= 104
5	35	20	10	= 65

X	6	10	9	Total
6	36	60	54	= 150
7	42	70	63	= 175
3	18	30	27	= 75
5	30	50	45	= 125

4. a. 20, 1, 10, 2, 5, 4
   b. 24, 1, 6, 4, 8, 3, 2, 12
   c. 21, 1, 7, 3
   d. 100, 1, 10, 20, 5, 25, 4, 50, 2

5. 100 cm

notes, practice and workings out

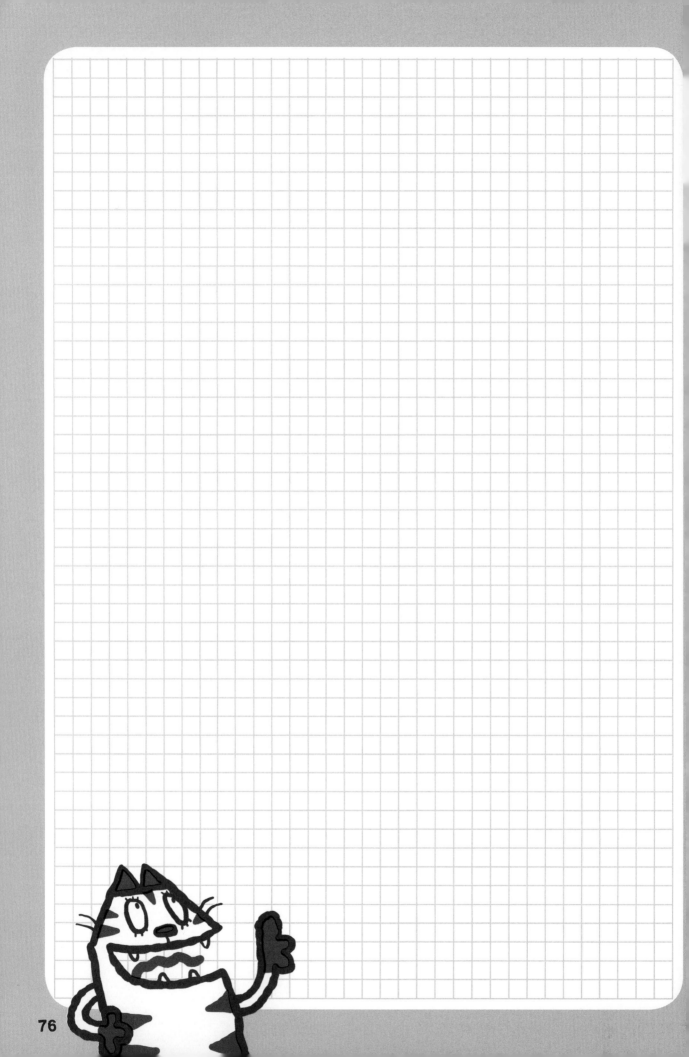

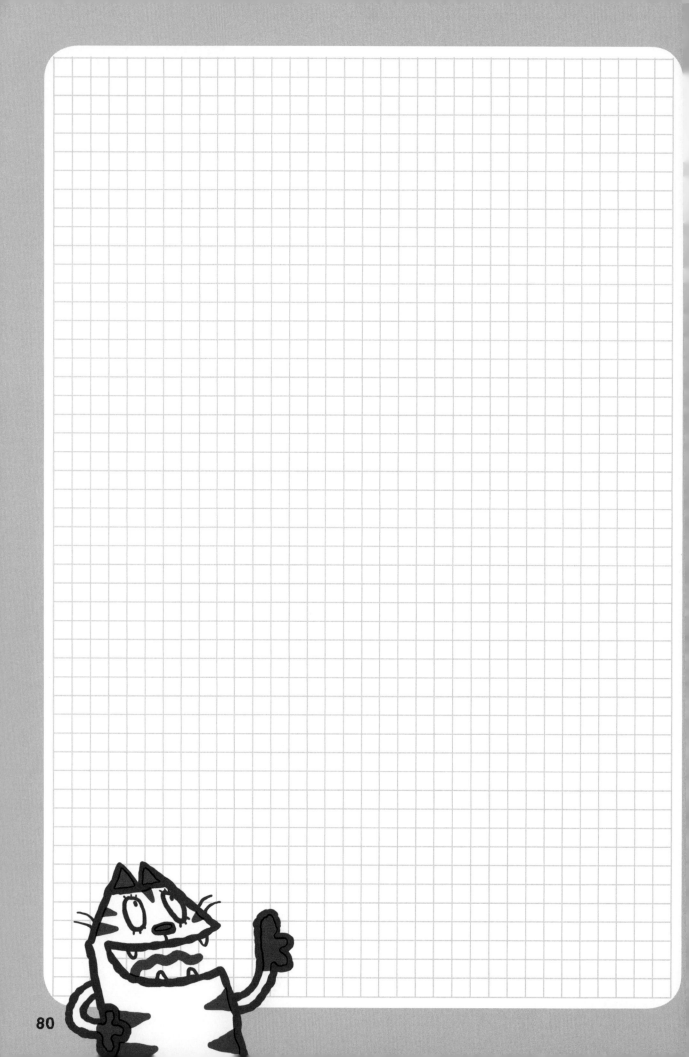

Maths

test time

numbers

Write these numbers in words.

a. 17

_____

b. 58

_____

c. 109

_____

d. 235

_____

e. 1302

_____

f. 5876

_____

g. 8219

_____

h. 4532

_____

i. 7925

_____

j. 5429

_____

k. 401

_____

l. 2416

_____

m. 446

_____

n. 10,245

_____

o. 21,899

_____

/15

test 2

more numbers

Write these numbers in numerals.

a. Three thousand, four hundred and two

_____

b. Seven thousand, eight hundred and seventy

_____

c. Twelve thousand, three hundred and six

_____

d. Forty thousand, nine hundred and sixty-six

_____

e. Three hundred and eight thousand, two hundred and twenty

_____

f. Fourteen thousand, seven hundred and twenty-one

_____

g. Two hundred and six thousand, four hundred and seventeen

_____

h. Ten thousand, three hundred and eighty

_____

Order these numbers from the smallest to the biggest.

i. 405, 543, 201, 333

_____

j. 902, 98, 299, 639

_____

k. 7843, 9287, 4900, 5912

_____

l. 6723, 7825, 9835, 1056

_____

m. 3333, 8324, 2338, 9273

_____

number values

Order these decimals from the smallest to the biggest.

a. 0.45, 0.73, 0.22, 0.98

_____

b. 0.03, 0.06, 0.89, 0.25

_____

c. 0.67, 0.91, 0.88, 0.04

_____

d. 0.92, 0.76, 0.04, 0.12

_____

e. 0.87, 0.01, 0.03, 0.77

_____

f. 0.6, 1.67, 0.67, 6.7

_____

g. 9.88, 8.99, 3.72, 4.03

_____

h. 4.89, 0.44, 3.29, 0.56

_____

i. 8.22, 5.10, 2.11, 0.09

_____

j. 5.54, 0.93, 7.23, 1.11

_____

k. 6.98, 3.77, 0.54, 4.76

_____

l. 2.34, 2.45, 2.67, 2.98

_____

m. 0.38, 3.23, 4.98, 1.22

_____

n. 0.09, 0.08, 0.54, 0.11

_____

o. 12.89, 34.41, 52.99, 39.76

_____

/15

test 4

number values

Order these numbers from left to right as they would appear on a number line.

a. 5, -7, 8, -9, -3, 2

_____

b. -3, 5, -4, -5, 7, 1

_____

c. 1, -5, -8, -2, 7, -7

_____

d. -5, 4, 7, 8, -12, -11

_____

e. 7, -7, 5, 11, -1, 8

_____

f. -13, 29, -20, 8, -14, 5

_____

g. 0, -12, 4, -8, -15, 6

_____

h. -8, -3, -12, 9, 15, 20

_____

i. -19, -2, 23, 5, -6, -1

_____

j. 3, 5, -12, 6, -18, 11

_____

k. 6, 60, -6, -16, 66, -66

_____

l. 4, 14, 44, 45, -4, -14

_____

m. -56, -75, -87, 33, -65, 21

_____

n. -100, -123, -37, 2, -6, 79

_____

o. 1, -1, -0.01, -10, -100, 100

_____

more number values

Which is more:

a. 7 hundreds or 77 tens

b. 54 tens or 6 hundreds

c. 2 hundreds or 1 ten and 9 units?

Which is less:

d. 12 tens or 2 hundreds

e. 5 thousands or 50 tens?

Calculate the following:

f. 3480….. 10 more is _____

g. 2365….. 10 more is _____

h. 3422….. 10 less is _____

i. 876….. 10 less is _____

j. 189….. 10 less is _____

k. 564….. 100 more is _____

l. 1278….. 100 more is _____

m. 777….. 100 less is _____

n. 2397….. 1000 more is _____

o. 9854….. 1000 less is _____

What is the biggest number you can make with these digits:

p. 3218 _____

q. 6901 _____

r. 5386 _____

s. 1154 _____

t. 7821? _____

addition and subtraction

Add these numbers:

a.
```
  H  T  U
     4  5
+ 2  5  4
_____

_____
```

b.
```
  H  T  U
  9  7  5
+    3  1
_____

_____
```

c.
```
  H  T  U
  3  2  4
+ 5  6  4
_____

_____
```

d.
```
Th H  T  U
 6  0  2  2
+1  0  4  3
_____

_____
```

e.
```
Th H  T  U
 7  0  3  5
-5  0  6  6
_____

_____
```

f.
```
Th H  T  U
 6  3  3  1
-2  0  0  1
_____

_____
```

Find the total of:

g. $24 + 450 + 3 =$ _____

h. $52 + 607 + 33 =$ _____

i. $9 + 22 + 42 + 90 =$ _____

j. $453 + 67 + 900 =$ _____

k. $760 + 3452 + 40 =$ _____

l. $5671 + 462 + 12 + 50 =$ _____

m. $77 + 112 + 9388 =$ _____

n. $560 - 14 - 3 =$ _____

o. $8992 - 549 =$ _____

/15

shapes

Name these 2-D and 3-D shapes.

a.

b.

c.

_____

d.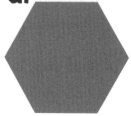

e.

f.

g.

_____

h.

i.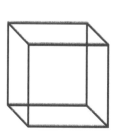

j.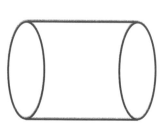

_____

/10

multiples and factors

a. Count in 3s:

3, _, 9, 12, 15, _, 21, 24, _, 30

b. Count in 4s:

_, 8, 12, _, 20, 24, 28, _, 36, _

c. Count in 5s:

5, 10, _, 20, 25, _, 35, 40, _, 50

d. Count in 8s:

8, _, 24, 32, _, _, 56, 64, _, 80

e. Count in 10s:

10, _, 30, _, _, 60, _, 80, _, _

f. Circle the numbers that are multiples of 8:

70   64   52   45   40   73

g. Circle the numbers that are multiples of 7:

55   48   49   17   77   42

h. Find factors of 48:

1 x 48
2 x _
4 x _
6 x _

i. Find factors of 60:

1 x _
2 x _
3 x _
5 x _
6 x _

j. Find factors of 18:

1 x _
2 x _
3 x _
6 x _
9 x _

/10

multiplication

Complete these multiplication grids.

a

X	2	5	6	3	9
4					
5					
2					
8					
10					

b

X	3	6	9	1	2
4					
7					
9					
1					
3					

c

X	4	8	2	1	9
9					
5					
7					
8					
1					

test 10

division

Answer these division sums.

a. $72 \div 8 = \boxed{}$

b. $45 \div 9 = \boxed{}$

c. $36 \div \boxed{} = 6$

d. $\boxed{} \div 7 = 11$

e. $\boxed{} \div 8 = 8$

f. $81 \div 9 = \boxed{}$

g. $\boxed{} \div 9 = 2$

h. $35 \div \boxed{} = 5$

i. $32 \div 8 = \boxed{}$

j. $100 \div 10 = \boxed{}$

k. $\boxed{} \div 3 = 7$

l. $12 \div 4 = \boxed{}$

m. $55 \div \boxed{} = 11$

n. $27 \div \boxed{} = 9$

o. $15 \div 5 = \boxed{}$

p. $99 \div \boxed{} = 11$

q. $10 \div \boxed{} = 2$

r. $\boxed{} \div 4 = 4$

s. $\boxed{} \div 3 = 3$

t. $20 \div 4 = \boxed{}$

20

95

test 11

perimeter

Find the perimeter of these shapes.

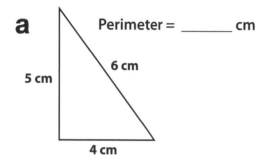

a Perimeter = _____ cm

5 cm
6 cm
4 cm

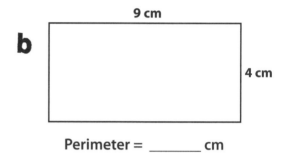

b

9 cm

4 cm

Perimeter = _____ cm

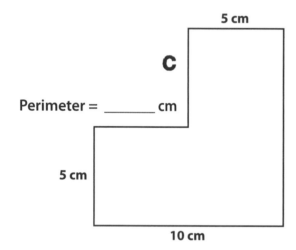

c

5 cm

Perimeter = _____ cm

5 cm

10 cm

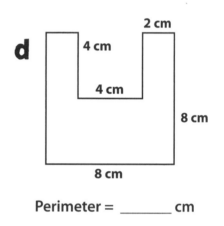

d

2 cm

4 cm

4 cm

8 cm

8 cm

Perimeter = _____ cm

Work out the perimeter of each of these regular polygons.

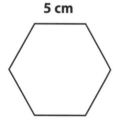

e

5 cm

Perimeter = _____ cm

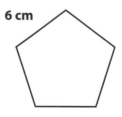

f

6 cm

Perimeter = _____ cm

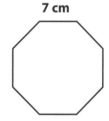

g

7 cm

Perimeter = _____ cm

/7

test 12

area

Find the area of these shapes.

a

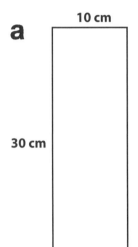

10 cm

30 cm

Area = _____ cm²

b

Area = _____ cm²

28 cm

7 cm

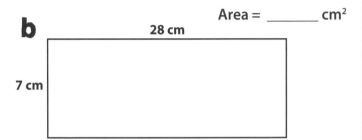

c

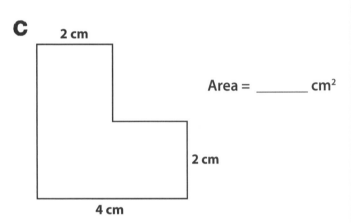

2 cm

Area = _____ cm²

2 cm

4 cm

d

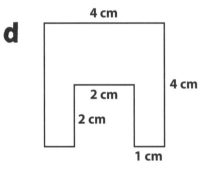

4 cm

4 cm

2 cm

2 cm

1 cm

Area = _____ cm²

e

19 cm

3 cm

Area = _____ cm²

f

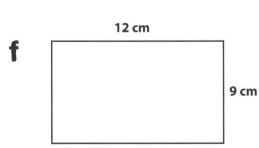

12 cm

9 cm

Area = _____ cm²

g

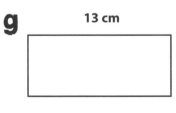

13 cm

5 cm

Area = _____ cm²

/7

97

test 13

fractions

Simplify these fractions:

a. $\dfrac{2}{18}$ = ——

b. $\dfrac{6}{36}$ = ——

c. $\dfrac{12}{24}$ = ——

d. $\dfrac{3}{12}$ = ——

e. $\dfrac{7}{21}$ = ——

f. $\dfrac{14}{28}$ = ——

g. $\dfrac{5}{25}$ = ——

h. $\dfrac{9}{27}$ = ——

i. $\dfrac{4}{16}$ = ——

j. $\dfrac{6}{60}$ = ——

k. $\dfrac{2}{20}$ = ——

l. $\dfrac{15}{30}$ = ——

Work out the answers.

m. $\dfrac{1}{2}$ of 60 =

n. $\dfrac{1}{4}$ of 24 =

o. $\dfrac{1}{8}$ of 48 =

p. $\dfrac{2}{3}$ of 21 =

q. $\dfrac{1}{5}$ of £3.50 =

r. $\dfrac{3}{4}$ of 20p =

s. $\dfrac{2}{3}$ of £27 =

t. $\dfrac{4}{5}$ of 25p =

20

fractions and percentages

Work out the answers:

a. 50% of 50 = _____

b. 25% of £8 = _____

c. 10% of 90 = _____

d. 10% of £9 = _____

e. 40% of 40p = _____

f. 20% of 22p = _____

g. 90% of 100cm = _____

h. 20% of 1 kg = _____

i. 5% of 50 ml = _____

j. 75% of £32 = _____

Join the fractions that have the same value.

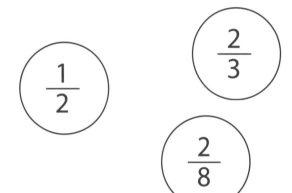

$\frac{2}{6}$

$\frac{9}{12}$ $\frac{3}{4}$

$\frac{1}{2}$ $\frac{2}{3}$

$\frac{2}{8}$

$\frac{5}{10}$ $\frac{1}{3}$

$\frac{6}{9}$

$\frac{1}{4}$ 15

test 15

more fractions

Colour these fractions of the shapes.

a Colour $\frac{1}{2}$

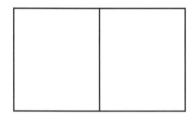

b Colour $\frac{1}{3}$

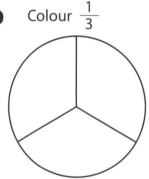

c Colour $\frac{3}{4}$

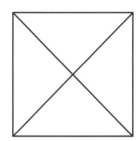

d Colour $\frac{2}{5}$

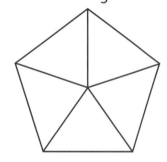

e Colour $\frac{5}{6}$

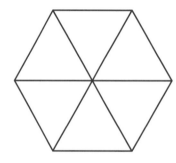

f Colour $\frac{1}{4}$

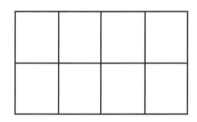

What fractions of these shapes are shaded?

g

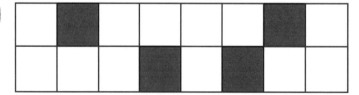

h

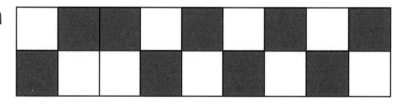

test 16

angles and triangles

Work out the missing angles in these triangles.

Write the names of these types of triangles.

a

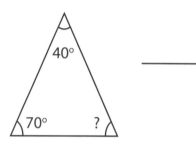

40°

70°   ?

_____

b

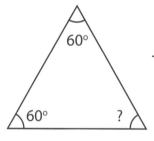

60°

60°   ?

_____

c

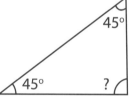

45°

45°   ?

_____

d

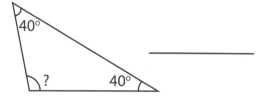

40°

?   40°

_____

e

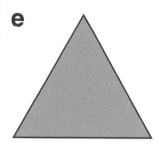

_____

f

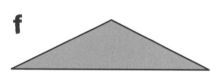

_____

g

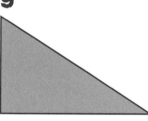

_____

h

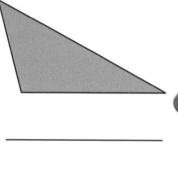

_____

/8

test 17

long multiplication

Use your preferred method to answer these multiplications. Remember to use the blank pages at the end of this section for any workings out.

a

```
  H  T  U
     2  1  8
x       2  1
_____
               (x20)

               (x1)
_____
```

b

```
  H  T  U
     3  4  5
x       1  7
_____
               (x10)

               (x7)
_____
```

c

```
  H  T  U
     6  4  3
x       2  2
_____
               (x20)

               (x2)
_____
```

d

```
  H  T  U
     2  5  4
x       1  5
_____
               (x10)

               (x5)
_____
```

e

```
  H  T  U
     6  4  3
x       2  3
_____
               (x20)

               (x3)
_____
```

/5

more long multiplication

Use your preferred method to answer these multiplications.

a

```
      H  T  U
      4  2  2
  x      2  7
  _____
                (x20)

                (x7)
  _____
```

b

```
      H  T  U
      9  9  3
  x      1  2
  _____
                (x10)

                (x12)
  _____
```

c

```
      H  T  U
      2  1  9
  x      3  5
  _____
                (x30)

                (x5)
  _____
```

d

```
      H  T  U
      5  2  0
  x      1  5
  _____
                (x10)

                (x5)
  _____
```

e

```
      H  T  U
      8  6  1
  x      2  2
  _____
                (x20)

                (x2)
  _____
```

/5

long division

Work out these divisions.

a

23 | 2 7 6

b

11 | 6 9 4

c

24 | 1 9 2

d

36 | 7 5 6

e

19 | 6 1 1

f

7 | 7 0 8

g

50 | 9 5 0

h

14 | 3 5 0

i

20 | 6 0 0

j

4 | 2 0 0 4

k

17 | 9 4 5

l

8 | 4 6 9

m

4 | 2 7 2

n

7 | 4 9 6

o

5 | 1 0 2 5

/15

test 20

decimals

Circle the decimal that is bigger in each pair.

a. 0.4   or   0.1

b. 2.3   or   9.8

c. 4.9   or   5.9

d. 3.5   or   5.3

e. 0.7   or   7.7

f. 6.5   or   5.9

g. 9.9   or   9.1

h. 5.2   or   2.5

i. 10.4 or   11

j. 12.9 or   19.2

k. 3.4   or   3.5

l. 22.3 or   23.1

m. 17.8 or   9.7

n. 22.0 or   21.9

14

add and subtract decimals

a
```
   0 . 7
 + 0 . 5
 ───────

```

b
```
   5 . 9
 + 3 . 3
 ───────

```

c
```
   0 . 9
 + 6 . 9
 ───────

```

d
```
   9 . 9
 + 0 . 4
 ───────

```

e
```
   2 . 8 5
 + 3 . 6 7
 ─────────

```

f
```
   4 . 8 7
 − 1 . 5 6
 ─────────

```

g
```
   6 . 6 9
 − 3 . 3 3
 ─────────

```

h
```
   4 . 6 8
 − 3 . 5 1
 ─────────

```

i
```
   9 . 3 4
 − 7 . 2 3
 ─────────

```

j
```
   18 . 2 2
 −  9 . 4 9
 ──────────

```

/10

decimals and money

Multiply and divide these decimals.

a. £3.50 x 5

f. Share £54.45 between 9 people.

b. £7.75 ÷ 5

g. Share £6.54 between 6 people

c. Share £15.27 between 3 people.

h. £3.04 x 7

d. £24.32 ÷ 8

i. 98p x 9

e. 7 lots of 75p

j. Share £12.84 between 4 people.

more decimals

Write these decimals in order from the smallest to the biggest.

a. 5.3, 9.2, 6.0, 7.1

_____ _____ _____ _____

b. 86p, £2.76, £2.56, 98p

_____ _____ _____ _____

c. 25cm, 2.5cm, 0.25cm, 2.1cm

_____ _____ _____ _____

d. 7.8m, 3.8m, 1.2m, 97cm

_____ _____ _____ _____

e. 2.9, 29.0, 0.29, 27.9

_____ _____ _____ _____

Find out:

f. How many centimetres in 3.6 metres?

_____ cm

g. What is 455cm in metres?

_____ m

h. How many millilitres in 2.3 litres?

_____ml

i. What comes next? 3.2, 3.4, 3.6, 3.8,

_____, _____

j. What comes next? 8.4, 8.1, 7.8, 7.5,

_____, _____

decimals and fractions

Draw a line to join each decimal to its fraction equivalent.

a.   b.   c.   d.   e.   f.

| 0.33 | 0.03 | 0.21 | 0.47 | 0.01 | 0.7 |

| $\frac{3}{100}$ | $\frac{21}{100}$ | $\frac{70}{100}$ | $\frac{33}{100}$ | $\frac{47}{100}$ | $\frac{1}{100}$ |

Try these:

g. What decimal is equivalent to 1/4? _____

h. What decimal is equivalent to 1/5? _____

i. What decimal is equivalent to ½? _____

j. What fraction is equivalent to 0.1? _____

k. What fraction is equivalent to 0.01? _____

Write these decimals on the number line.

l. 0.3   **m.** 1.4   **n.** 1.9   **o.** 0.7   **p.** 1.0

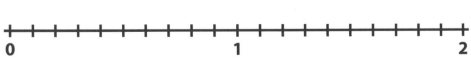

16

x and ÷ 10 and 100

Work out the following:

a. 7   x   10   = _____

b. 22   x   10   = _____

c. 650   x   10   = _____

d. 80   ÷   10   = _____

e. 3500 ÷   10   = _____

f. 97   x   10   = _____

g. 540   ÷   10   = _____

h. 32   x   10   = _____

i. 651   x   10   = _____

j. 780   ÷   10   = _____

Now work out the following:

k. 3   x   100 = _____

l. 8   x   100 = _____

m. 25   x   100 = _____

n. 2000 ÷ 100 = _____

o. 300   ÷ 100 = _____

p. 234   x   100 = _____

q. 49   x   100 = _____

r. 100   ÷ 100 = _____

s. 12   x   100 = _____

t. 6450 ÷ 10   = _____

20

test 26

more x and ÷ 10 and 100

Calculate the following:

a. One-tenth of 110 is _____

b. Two-tenths of 300 is _____

c. Three-tenths of 220 _____

d. One-hundredth of 700 is _____

e. Three-tenths of 40 is _____

f. Five-tenths (or ½) of £2.50 is _____

g. Five-hundredths of £2 is _____

h. One-tenth of £80 is _____

i. One-tenth of 90kg is _____

j. One-tenth of 45kg is _____

k. Two-tenths of 60p is _____

l. One-hundredth of 6kg is _____

m. One-hundredth of £500 is _____

n. Three-tenths of 50 is _____

o. Five-tenths (or ½) of 24kg is _____

p. One-tenth of 1000 is _____

q. Three-tenths of 1000 is _____

r. Two-tenths of £4000 is _____

measures

Solve these problems.

a. The high-jumper jumped 4.6m.
How high is that in centimetres? _____cm

b. The dog ran 3.9km. How far is that in metres? _____m

c. 25mm = _____centimetres

d. 4.7 litres = _____ millilitres

e. What is 15kg as grams? _____g

f. Half a metre = _____ centimetres

g. Convert 4.3cm to millimetres. _____ mm

h. Which is shorter: 600mm or 6cm? _____

i. The bag weighs 7.3kg. How much is that in grams? _____g

j. Half a litre = _____ millilitres

k. 5.87m = _____ centimetres

l. What is 7520g in kilograms? _____kg

m. 3.56km = _____metres

n. Daisy has a watering can that contains 6 litres of water. She also has 2 small jugs that carry 2 litres of water each. How many millilitres of water can she carry altogether? _____ml

o. Dan cycled 4.5km and then pushed his bike up a hill for a further 750 metres. How many kilometres did he travel altogether? _____ km

15

graphs

Look at the pie chart that shows the way children travel to school in Year 5.

There are 64 children in Year 5.

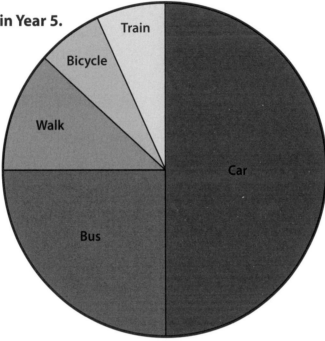

Answer the following questions based on the chart.

a. Which is the most popular way of travelling to school? _____

b. Which is the least popular way of travelling to school?_____

c. What percentage of children travel to school by car? _____%

d. What percentage of children do not travel by car or bus? _____%

e. How many children travel by bus? _____

f. How many children travel by bicycle? _____

mix it up!

a. Write this number in words.

589,210 _____

b. Order these numbers from smallest to largest.

20,301   202   0.23   2033   0.02   32

_____

c. Work out the answers to these sums.

```
    5  2  7  5              3  4  2  1
 +  2  2  5  5           -  1  3  8  8
 _____          _____

 _____          _____
```

d. John went shopping for his sister, Amy. He only bought two of the items on Amy's shopping list.

> **Shopping list:**
> blue purse £3.50
> small comb £3.15
> red hairband £2.75

He had £3.75 change from £10. Which two items did he buy?

_____

e. What are the next two numbers in the sequence?

2.2, 3.2, 4.2, _____, _____   Rule is _____

test 30

mix it up!

a. Name these shapes.

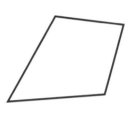 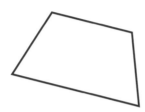 

_____   _____   _____

b. How many vertices does a cuboid have?

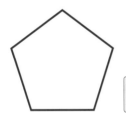   _____

c. Tick the shape that has 6 lines of symmetry.

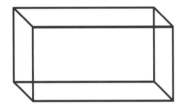

d. Write two divisions to match this multiplication.
8 x 7 = 56

_____   _____

e. An acute angle is larger than a right angle.
True or false? _____

5

answers

test 1

a. seventeen
b. fifty-eight
c. one hundred and nine
d. two hundred and thirty-five
e. one thousand, three hundred and two
f. five thousand, eight hundred and seventy-six
g. eight thousand, two hundred and nineteen
h. four thousand, five hundred and thirty-two
i. seven thousand, nine hundred and twenty-five
j. five thousand, four hundred and twenty-nine
k. four hundred and one
l. two thousand, four hundred and sixteen
m. four hundred and forty-six

test 2

a. 3402
b. 7870
c. 12,306
d. 40,966
e. 308,220
f. 14,721
g. 206,417
h. 10,380
i. 201, 333, 405, 543
j. 98, 299, 639, 902
k. 4900, 5912, 7843, 9287
l. 1056, 6723, 7825, 9835
m. 2338, 3333, 8324, 9273

test 3

a. 0.22, 0.45, 0.73, 0.98
b. 0.03, 0.06, 0.25, 0.89
c. 0.04, 0.67, 0.88, 0.91
d. 0.04, 0.12, 0.76, 0.92
e. 0.01, 0.03, 0.77, 0.87
f. 0.6, 0.67, 1.67, 6.7
g. 3.72, 4.03, 8.99, 9.88
h. 0.44, 0.56, 3.29, 4.89
i. 0.09, 2.11, 5.10, 8.22
j. 0.93, 1.11, 5.54, 7.23
k. 0.54, 3.77, 4.76, 6.98
l. 2.34, 2.45, 2.67, 2.98
m. 0.38, 1.22, 3.23, 4.98
n. 0.08, 0.09, 0.11, 0.54
o. 12.89, 34.41, 39.76, 52.99

test 4

a. -9, -7, -3, 2, 5, 8
b. -5, -4, -3, 1, 5, 7
c. -8, -7, -5, -2, 1, 7
d. -12, -11, -5, 4, 7, 8
e. -7, -1, 5, 7, 8, 11
f. -20, -14, -13, 5, 8, 29
g. -15, -12, -8, 0, 4, 6
h. -12, -8, -3, 9, 15, 20
i. -19, -6, -2, -1, 5, 23
j. -18, -12, 3, 5, 6, 11
k. -66, -16, -6, 6, 60, 66
l. -14, -4, 4, 14, 44, 45
m. -87, -75, -65, -56, 21, 33
n. -123, -100, -37, -6, 2, 79
o. -100, -10, -1, -0.01, 1, 100

test 5

a. 77 tens is more
b. 6 hundreds is more
c. 2 hundreds is more
d. 12 tens is less
e. 50 tens is less

f. 3490
g. 2375
h. 3412
i. 866
j. 179
k. 664
l. 1378
m. 677

n. 3397
o. 8854

p. 8321
q. 9610
r. 8653
s. 5411
t. 8721

HOW HAVE YOU DONE SO FAR?

test 6

a. 299
b. 1006
c. 888
d. 7065
e. 1969
f. 4330
g. 477
h. 692
i. 163
j. 1420
k. 4252
l. 6195
m. 9577
n. 543
o. 8443

answers

test 7

a. parallelogram
b. trapezium
c. square
d. (regular) hexagon
e. triangle
f. rhombus
g. (regular) pentagon
h. cone
i. cube
j. cylinder

test 11

a. 15cm
b. 26cm
c. 40cm
d. 40cm
e. 30cm
f. 30cm
g. 56cm

test 8

a. 3, 6, 9, 12, 15, 18, 21, 24, 27 , 30
b. 4, 8, 12, 16, 20, 24, 28, 32, 36, 40
c. 5, 10, 15, 20, 25, 30, 35, 40, 45, 50
d. 8, 16, 24, 32, 40, 48, 56, 64, 72, 80
e. 10, 20, 30, 40, 50, 60, 70, 80, 90, 100

f. 70 (64) 52 45 (40) 73
g. 55 48 (49) 17 (77) (42)
h. 1 x 48 / 2 x 24 / 4 x 12 / 6 x 8
i. 1 x 60 / 2 x 30 / 3 x 20 / 5 x 12 / 6 x 10
j. Find factors of 18: 1 x 18 / 2 x 9 / 3 x 6 / 6 x 3 / 9 x 2

test 12

a. 300cm²
b. 196cm²
c. 12cm²
d. 12cm²
e. 57cm²
f. 108cm²
g. 65cm²

test 9

a.

X	2	5	6	3	9
4	8	20	24	12	36
5	10	25	30	15	45
2	4	10	12	6	18
8	16	40	48	24	72
10	20	50	60	30	90

b.

X	3	6	9	1	2
4	12	24	36	4	8
7	21	42	63	7	14
9	27	54	81	9	18
1	3	6	9	1	2
3	9	18	27	3	6

c.

X	4	8	2	1	9
9	36	72	18	9	81
5	20	40	10	5	45
7	28	56	14	7	63
8	32	64	16	8	72
1	4	8	2	1	9

test 13

a. $\frac{2}{18} = \frac{1}{9}$
b. $\frac{6}{36} = \frac{1}{6}$
c. $\frac{12}{24} = \frac{1}{2}$
d. $\frac{3}{12} = \frac{1}{4}$
e. $\frac{7}{21} = \frac{1}{3}$
f. $\frac{14}{28} = \frac{1}{2}$
g. $\frac{5}{25} = \frac{1}{5}$
h. $\frac{9}{27} = \frac{1}{3}$
i. $\frac{4}{16} = \frac{1}{4}$
j. $\frac{6}{60} = \frac{1}{10}$
k. $\frac{2}{20} = \frac{1}{10}$
l. $\frac{15}{30} = \frac{1}{2}$
m. $\frac{1}{2}$ of 60 = 30
n. $\frac{1}{4}$ of 24 = 6
o. $\frac{1}{8}$ of 48 = 6
p. $\frac{2}{3}$ of 21 = 14
q. $\frac{1}{5}$ of £3.50 = 70p
r. $\frac{3}{4}$ of 20p = 15p
s. $\frac{2}{3}$ of £27 = £18
t. $\frac{4}{5}$ of 25p = 20p

test 10

a. 72 ÷ 8 = 9
b. 45 ÷ 9 = 5
c. 36 ÷ 6 = 6
d. 77 ÷ 7 = 11
e. 64 ÷ 8 = 8
f. 81 ÷ 9 = 9
g. 18 ÷ 9 = 2
h. 35 ÷ 7 = 5
i. 32 ÷ 8 = 4
j. 100 ÷ 10 = 10
k. 21 ÷ 3 = 7
l. 12 ÷ 4 = 3
m. 55 ÷ 5 = 11
n. 27 ÷ 3 = 9
o. 15 ÷ 5 = 3
p. 99 ÷ 9 = 11
q. 10 ÷ 5 = 2
r. 16 ÷ 4 = 4
s. 9 ÷ 3 = 3
t. 20 ÷ 4 = 5

GIVE YOURSELF A PAT ON THE BACK!

test 14

a. 50% of 50 = 25
b. 25% of £8 = £2
c. 10% of 90 = 9
d. 10% of £9 = 90p
e. 40% of 40p = 16p
f. 20% of 22p = 4.4p
g. 90% of 100cm = 90cm
h. 20% of 1 kg = 200g
j. 5% of 50ml = 2.5ml
k. 75% of £32 = £24

$\frac{3}{4}$ — $\frac{9}{12}$

$\frac{1}{2}$ — $\frac{5}{10}$

$\frac{2}{3}$ — $\frac{6}{9}$

$\frac{1}{4}$ — $\frac{2}{8}$

$\frac{1}{3}$ — $\frac{2}{6}$

answers

test 15

a.
b.
c.

d.
e.
f.

g. $\frac{1}{4}$

h. $\frac{1}{2}$

test 16

a. 70°
b. 60°
c. 90°
d. 100°

e. equilateral
f. isosceles
g. right-angled
h. scalene

test 17

a. 4578
b. 5865
c. 14,146
d. 3810
e. 14,789

test 18

a. 11,394
b. 11,916
c. 7665
d. 7800
e. 18,942

test 19

a. 12
b. 63 r1
c. 8
d. 21
e. 32 r3
f. 101 r1
g. 19
h. 25
i. 30
j. 501
k. 55 r10
l. 58 r5
m. 68
n. 70 r6
o. 205

test 20

a. 0.4
b. 9.8
c. 5.9
d. 5.3
e. 7.7
f. 6.5
g. 9.9
h. 5.2
i. 11
j. 19.2
k. 3.5
l. 23.1
m. 17.8
n. 22.0

test 21

a. 1.2
b. 9.2
c. 7.8
d. 10.3
e. 6.52
f. 3.31
g. 3.36
h. 1.17
i. 2.11
j. 8.73

test 22

a. £17.50
b. £1.55
c. £5.09
d. £3.04
e. £5.25
f. £6.05
g. £1.09
h. £21.28
i. £8.82
j. £3.21

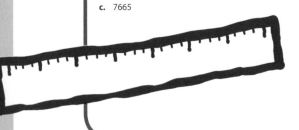

answers

test 23

a. 5.3, 6.0, 7.1, 9.2
b. 86p, 98p, £2.56, £2.76
c. 0.25 cm, 2.1 cm, 2.5cm, 25cm
d. 97cm, 1.2m, 3.8m, 7.8m
e. 0.29, 2.9, 27.9, 29.0
f. 360cm
g. 4.55m
h. 2300 ml
i. 3.2, 3.4, 3.6, 3.8, 4.0, 4.2
j. 8.4, 8.1, 7.8, 7.5, 7.2, 6.9

KEEP PRACTISING!

test 24

a. $0.33 - \frac{33}{100}$
b. $0.03 - \frac{3}{100}$
c. $0.21 - \frac{21}{100}$
d. $0.47 - \frac{47}{100}$
e. $0.01 - \frac{1}{100}$
f. $0.7 - \frac{70}{100}$

g. 0.25   h. 0.2   i. 0.5   j. ¹⁄₁₀   k. ¹⁄₁₀₀

l. 0.3   o. 0.7   p. 1.0   m. 1.4   n. 1.9

(number line 0 to 2)

test 25

a. 7 x 10 = 70
b. 22 x 10 = 220
c. 650 x 10 = 6500
d. 80 ÷ 10 = 8
e. 3500 ÷ 10 = 350
f. 97 x 10 = 970
g. 540 ÷ 10 = 54
h. 32 x 10 = 320
i. 651 x 10 = 6510
j. 780 ÷ 10 = 78
k. 3x 100 = 300
l. 8 x 100 = 800
m. 25 x 100 = 2500
n. 2000 ÷ 100 = 20
o. 300 ÷ 100 = 3
p. 234 x 100 = 23,400
q. 49 x 100 = 4900
r. 100 ÷ 100 = 1
s. 12 x 100 = 1200
t. 6450 ÷ 10 = 645

test 26

a. 11
b. 60
c. 66
d. 7
e. 12
f. £1.25
g. 10p
h. £8
i. 9kg
j. 4.5kg
k. 12p
l. 60g
m. £5
n. 15
o. 12kg
p. 100
q. 300
r. £800

YOU'RE THE BEST!

test 27

a. 460cm
b. 3900m
c. 2.5 centimetres
d. 4700 millilitres
e. 1500g
f. 50 centimetres
g. 43mm
h. 6cm
i. 7300g
j. 500 millilitres
k. 587 centimetres
l. 7.52kg
m. 3560 metres
n. 10,000ml
o. 5.25km

test 28

a. car
b. train and bicycle
c. 50%
d. 25%
e. 16
f. 4

test 29

a. five hundred and eighty-nine thousand, two hundred and ten
b. 0.02 0.23 32 202 2033 20,301
c. 7530 2033
d. blue purse and red hairband
e. 5.2, 6.2 (rule is add 1)

test 30

a. kite, trapezium, square-based pyramid
b. 8
c.
d. 56 ÷ 7 = 8   56 ÷ 8 = 7
e. false

practice, practice practice!

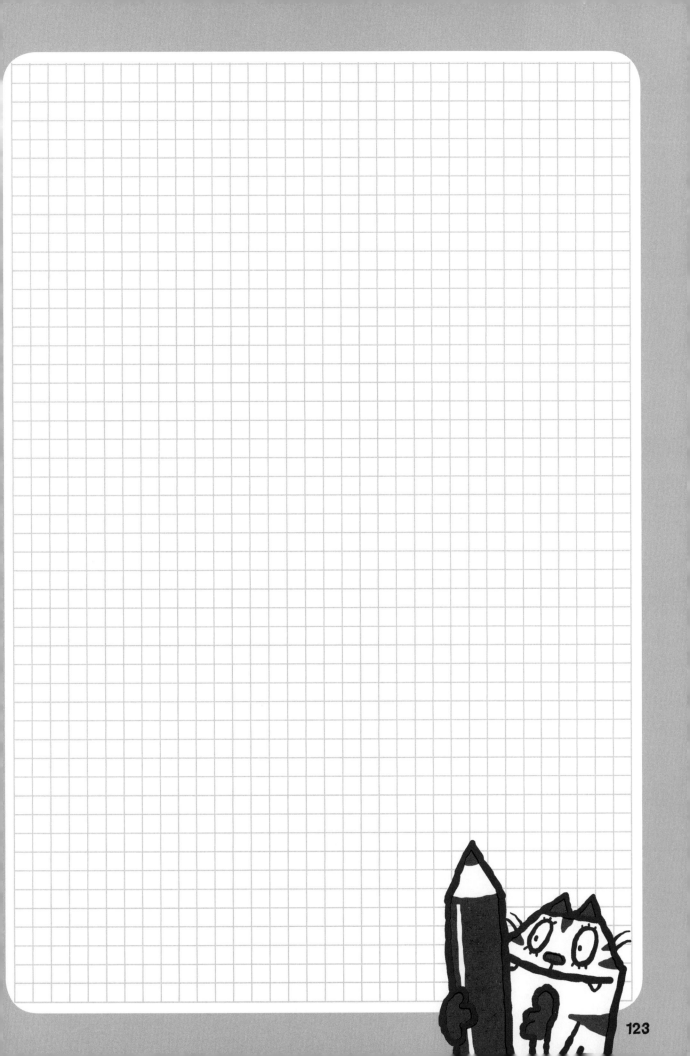

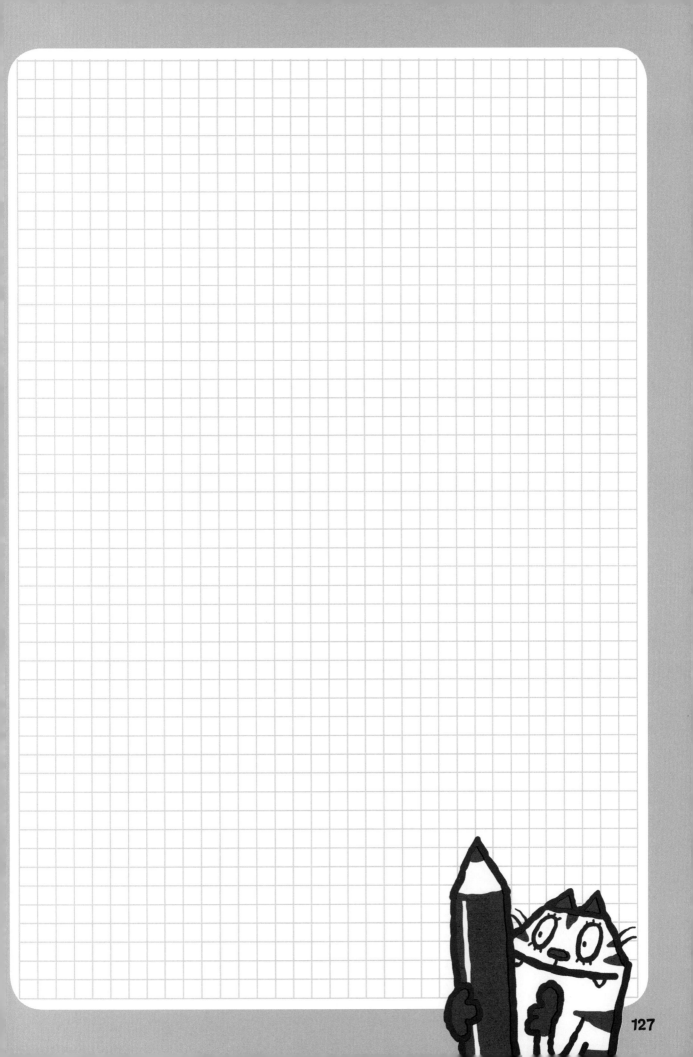

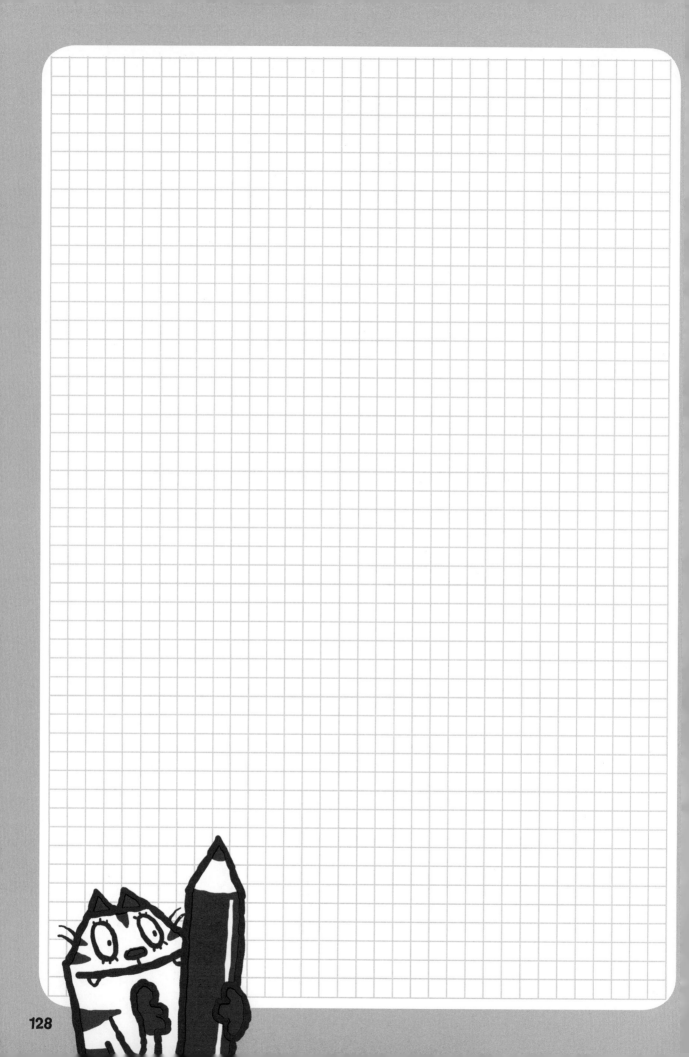